DAILY MAIL CROSSWORD BOOK
VOLUME FIVE

Also published

Daily Mail Quick Crossword Book

Daily Mail
Crossword Book
Volume Five

HEADLINE

First published in 1998
by HEADLINE BOOK PUBLISHING

10 9 8

ISBN 0 7472 5705 1

Typeset by Michael Mepham, Frome, Somerset
Printed and bound in Great Britain by
Mackays of Chatham plc, Chatham, Kent

HEADLINE BOOK PUBLISHING
A division of Hodder HeadlinePLC
338 Euston Road
London NW1 3BH

Clues

1

ACROSS

1 Dashing for a buck (7)
5 Take the plunge and cause a sensation (6)
9 Light moved into line in a proper way (7)
10 Frank is certain to succeed (7)
11 Don't just stand there on the stage! (3)
12 Little room here for consumer satisfaction (11)
13 Manage to produce endless nonsense (5)
14 Tree given the bullet in the Army's place (9)
16 Orders to group to give a gun back (9)
17 Joke with a companion in drink (5)
19 Tied Captain in a knot as expected (11)
22 Try to put an end to scandal (3)
23 Celebrated some of them in entirely suitable ways (7)
24 Comfort old official who's had half a life inside (7)
26 More than a little protective of a good person in church (6)
27 Reveals attitudes no longer held (7)

DOWN

1 Flowers for Judy (7)
2 Impact of a storm causing a quick walk-out (9,6)
3 Clever at finding money inside (3)
4 Attempt to find a way to achieve a meeting (5)
5 Bright lights are hell – you need protection (3-6)
6 Means of communication among those contemplating divorce (5)
7 Exercise support at greater length (7,4,4)
8 Man on watch (6)
12 Sound girl to give a ring (5)
14 Incline hat awkwardly in whatever expresses dislike (9)
15 Run and get paid out in a hurry (5)
16 One's able to take in what's been set down (6)
18 Unfortunate if it should come to pass that you've only a pen (7)
20 Part of a body in a box (5)
21 A number you've got wrong there (5)
25 Do a round? You'll only make it if you sit down (3)

2

ACROSS

1 Swan not looking good having to dodge fish (4,8)
8 Go wrong with Dan's dodgy missions (7)
9 One chases a ship's officer round the bend (7)
11 They're expected to achieve soaring ambitions (4-6)
12 Gain five hundred at a blow (4)
14 Surpass in quality of open-air teaching (8)
16 Let's have that music again for a dance, my lord! (6)
17 Best give the trophy back (3)
19 For instance moving back without one being given a drink (6)
21 Battle station (8)
24 Great story rewritten from a short piece (4)
25 He's not much different from a man of Dee (10)
27 Virginia in the footsteps of Labour (7)
28 Metal bird to be seen in an abbey (7)
29 Still permanently rejecting subordination (12)

DOWN

1 Standing for what's honest (7)
2 Yearn to make a college chap a poet (10)
3 Having attracted the most deposits (8)
4 Skips exercise in transport (6)
5 Bird of paradise or similar kind (4)
6 Sustain in hours of trouble (7)
7 Removing from high position to operate the modern net (12)
10 Making a new arrangement that's revolutionary using a thousand less for work (12)
13 Passing allusion to how players might strike at an angle (4-6)
15 Broadcast from demonstration without getting hot (3)
18 Inventor carrying a number in his head to start engine (8)
20 Forbidding a star to look unfriendly (7)
22 They permit rises in the number of snakes (7)
23 See the Italian fool around when the scene is not quite dark (6)
26 Uncovered by lawyers at the end of the case (4)

ACROSS

6 Glove won't fit? Try this alternative (2,3,5,4)
9 Get away in case of trouble with people inwardly lacking (6)
10 Cur tries corrupting soldiers (8)
11 Having knowledge of old money dropped into the river the wrong way (8)
13 The business of love (6)
15 The party to beat (6)
17 Having power that rots badly is no good (6)
19 Drop a correct note – get real! (6)
20 Innocent user of under-cover shopping? (8)
22 A tyrant to his secretary? (8)
24 One has a child making payment to the old man (6)
26 There's something in it that isn't open to be read (6,8)

DOWN

1 Security person employed to find out if there's accommodation? (5,9)
2 Mount part of a secret naval strike (4)
3 Choose to be exclusive (6)
4 Foreign sea song one buys and sells (8)
5 You are singularly old-fashioned (4)
7 Make it a Red revolutionary rant (6)
8 Refusing to be discouraged by undoing that end in error (7,7)
12 Island business dealing with fur (5)
14 Too much liquidity gets a girl in debt to the bank (5)
16 Only one's own company is maintained in it (8)
18 Soldiers in a farm building producing nothing (6)
21 Metal obtainable for very little money (6)
23 Something to pay for the ring (4)
25 Right to low rise accommodation (4)

4

ACROSS

1 Ducks give approval for one that plumbs the depths (3-5)
5 The old chap in charge (6)
9 Mix-up in the enclosure (8)
10 Material needed if crab is to be cooked (6)
12 A lovely girl in England is hardly unusual (4)
13 Deem models to be unreliable and interfering (10)
15 L for London telling you something (7,6)
19 Firm with a lady who's into affairs (13)
23 Fall for the wrong set in a foreign environment (4-6)
25 Don't go on getting a lot of money back (4)
28 Wear out one good little creature (6)
29 Stakes to be paid with sale involved (8)
30 Point to rum left unfinished by the head (6)
31 A few words that may take time to work out (8)

DOWN

1 Make clear what was written by a poet last month (6)
2 Questions those that might be worn out dancing (5)
3 Make brisk progress in the wrong get-up (4)
4 Agree to be given a mission after study (7)
6 A tricky way to cause surprise (5)
7 Sacrifice time to catch up when out of one's mind (9)
8 Hard to start getting even with test missiles (8)
11 One old eccentric many admire (4)
14 Turn to the expertise of a political doctor (4)
15 Decommissioned by someone with money (9)
16 One hasn't the sense to get by without money (3)
17 She's got the measure of a person of degree (4)
18 Terrier town (8)
20 Try to reach the shore when you're on board (4)
21 Pay for work to protect a way that's no use (7)
22 Where there's work for an all-rounder? (6)
24 Decoration to excite careless talkers? (5)
26 Mark more than one writer (5)
27 Take up an offer of free transport (4)

5

ACROSS

1 Enterprise thriving on customer backing (7,4)
9 Hurried in new gear to produce order (7)
10 I find myself about to get by when unable to move (7)
11 Nothing will get one into a car from Holland (3)
12 Get someone who's up down (7)
13 Not exaggerating stories about drink (7)
14 In operation for a time (3)
15 Endless column dodging by a deputy (5)
17 Wanting a lot without starting to get shrill (5)
18 Old man out of bed for a quick rise (3-2)
20 More former pictures returned (5)
22 Garment you can have for a pound (3)
24 One doubts if copyright can be concealed by the corrupt (7)
25 One flies from the blackest religious persecution (7)
26 Visionary communicating to another in agreement (3)
27 Mostly Spanish tribe at last managed to take one in (7)
28 Smell not even experienced in town (7)
29 Accept as a director (4,2,5)

DOWN

1 Gift of survival for another year (8,7)
2 Shoot a number neglecting final training (7)
3 Peace figure showing anger at some points (5)
4 Blame wretched mole for going in as a diver (9)
5 This rep could be one of the beat generation (7)
6 Conduct a top circulation exercise to raise funds (4,3,3,5)
7 Put a hand up to show respect (6)
8 Island of bodily warmth (6)
16 End soccer disorder that's getting louder (9)
18 Drink permit – put it back inside (6)
19 Dodge after an assistant has made a name (7)
21 Its aura is unsuitable to the state (7)
23 Highball served up by retiring revolutionary (6)
25 One may be transfixed by the cook (5)

6

ACROSS

1 Sudden riser puts new version with skill (7)
5 Frighten rabbit (6)
9 Bore a number back to make a police search (7)
10 One's made a race around to gain height (7)
11 Informal talk of a strike (3)
12 He's one among family members who can get explanation put in (11)
13 Organs for the consumer (5)
14 No comfort without promotion in the army? (9)
16 Used to be thinking of demanding a lot of money (9)
17 Source of a donation (5)
19 Fierce cat – it needs new licence (11)
22 Point to Silver, the horse (3)
23 Satisfaction is very short in Greene's version (7)
24 Foreign airs needing sun to be played (7)
26 Some clothes provide a bit of cheap cover (6)
27 Trash the rest almost without hearing in grim fashion (7)

DOWN

1 Suffer to use the subway (7)
2 Showing you like to put your foot down? (5,2,8)
3 She cannot do without something for the baby (3)
4 Union eminence being the one to give instruction (5)
5 Credit one with sorting out what's obscure (9)
6 They may be taken out if false (5)
7 Thought of something quite new (6,9)
8 Some sort of voting is applied where there's no freedom (6)
12 Supporter of current power (5)
14 Awful gripe about disgraceful benefit (9)
15 Put the case for taking in some peculiar guests (5)
16 One goes with a change of corset (6)
18 Bucks time (7)
20 A number not entirely pleasant in style (5)
21 Hanging in a somewhat embarrassing place (5)
25 The woman he's going to ruin (3)

ACROSS

1 The way to get to where you want to be (8,4)
8 Difficult to see how bombing starts in course of revolution (7)
9 Investigators back in food examination (7)
11 Musicians from hell cause bewilderment (10)
12 Go round for a music hall act (4)
14 Suspicion, obscurity, deterioration (8)
16 Recorded as having been said by someone else (6)
17 Identification may be child's play (3)
19 Low jet crashing with cab (6)
21 They find there are characters on hand (8)
24 Land in the water (4)
25 Fish giving a girl food poisoning (10)
27 Two offers rejected in there perhaps (7)
28 Add frisky mice that have symbolic significance (7)
29 How to decide the best use of company biros (2,10)

DOWN

1 Helps when a beast of burden is taking the wrong way (7)
2 Wealth is the rule here (10)
3 Threatening to have done with players (8)
4 Arrived with an artist able to give you the picture (6)
5 Uncultured lady Gert takes off (4)
6 Story of where the money went (7)
7 Blame business needing to mend awful state (12)
10 Yearn to be first in taking steps to get far away (4-8)
13 Finishes with ten musical turns (10)
15 Sort of dancing an Irishman gets up to (3)
18 It may give some measure of what's cooking (3-5)
20 Something playful about marines (7)
22 Only one Scot could be such a wise one (7)
23 Weekend talk by the governor (6)
26 Go away and be quiet when there are rings (4)

6 ... where the score is nil (7)

11 A ... (6) ... to ... can have ...

13 ... of ... gets ...

14 ... Italy ... to be ... of ... (7)

19 ... a ... gun ... at a ... (6)

16 ... Gypsy ... name part of what school is (3)

20 Something mystical about manners (7)

22 Only one Scot could be such a wise one (7)

23 Weekend which the governor (6)

24 Go away and be quiet when there are things (4)

ACROSS

6 Villainous character in an unpleasant job (5,3,2,4)
9 Be slow to make progress (6)
10 Bit of a joke applied to people in short measure (8)
11 One turned round to start repelling gate-crasher (8)
13 Deny having to broadcast during a row (6)
15 Crush and devour having been given food back (6)
17 Turned red on finding girl romantic (6)
19 Please shake if not paying attention (6)
20 Making it quite clear there's water coming in at night? (8)
22 Hand out writing materials inside out (8)
24 Fruit and vegetable man at the ring (6)
26 What makes the difference is having an agent who knows his own mind (8,6)

DOWN

1 Hate starting at once (7,7)
2 Turn this way when invited to see the city (4)
3 One will come down in a winking (6)
4 Officer with royal person in a leaky vessel (8)
5 Sink alternative (4)
7 Failing in business (6)
8 Spectacular triumph in retreat? (7,7)
12 Go through with a gun (5)
14 Bear erect (5)
16 Additional matter for operational removal (8)
18 Feeble notes at a garden party (6)
21 Spending on free-range egg production (6)
23 Vessel making the old man almost sick (4)
25 Little creature of sound power (4)

ACROSS

1 Following without one having a month in church (8)
5 Having been crushed for some reason (6)
9 End of time in a late start (8)
10 Takes off for an outing in a ship (6)
12 In good time we reach a vessel (4)
13 Get an old driver to express approval about a disturbance (10)
15 Their get-together could get people singing (5,3,5)
19 Everything bad is down to money (4,2,3,4)
23 One doesn't charge for taking on board a parasite (10)
25 Earnest request for some apple and plum jam (4)
28 Hard to see if mockery is intended? (6)
29 Clear person on the condition set out (8)
30 Grovel and fawn to reduce friction (6)
31 Grown-up affairs? (8)

DOWN

1 Begin to fall for a rag-and-bone man (6)
2 Give consent in correspondence (5)
3 Garment supplied in error (4)
4 Becomes an informer with some juicy items (7)
6 Proportion seen to be in operation (5)
7 The sort of joint you see everywhere (9)
8 Area where a girl has to be firm (8)
11 Wave the dish away and have some cereal (4)
14 Breaking a rib does nothing for one's spirit (4)
15 Take the lot and only part is nourishing (9)
16 That's everything finished! (3)
17 Make a proposal that will inspire feeling (4)
18 Insignificant flirtation (8)
20 A girl who lacks finish, one's sorry to say (4)
21 A welder works to establish the wind direction (7)
22 Gasp at a line that makes room for the butler (6)
24 Retreats from an apprentice who gives himself affectations of superiority (5)
26 Loyal subject, say, caught in deceit (5)
27 It's swallowed quietly by the sick (4)

Find the solution is on page ...

5 ...
9 ...
12 ...
15 ...
17 ...
19 ... is on a banjo (7)
20 Imagination boundless (6)
Dodgy girl who is at stake, one's easy to spot (4)
24 A weather worn to ... up his loud lament (7)
26 ... but in the chair sufferes on first's better ...
28 Richard Bu ... appearance when ... film or theatrical ... of audience ... (...)
30 Royal ... quaint ... one's mistakes (9)
31 He swallows whereby ... on also (4)

ACROSS

1 Accommodation rejected as absolutely unacceptable (4,7)
9 It's a wonder you can see the way clear for movement (7)
10 One may decide to cook a rarebit (7)
11 One could hold beer in the cellar like good wine (3)
12 Abandons a number of irritants (7)
13 Given a seat after standing (7)
14 Bring back shelter for a swimmer (3)
15 See a visit cut short in the neighbourhood (5)
17 Agree to meet at last with an associate (5)
18 Fabulous fellow taking a backward attitude (5)
20 Scolded for having foreshadowed an unspeakable take-off (5)
22 A snob gets high on it (3)
24 Arrange to do spies' work (7)
25 One goes round with an invitation to have a bite (7)
26 Figure returned after deductions (3)
27 Most likely to make contact with a listener in the home (7)
28 Result of using an escape route (7)
29 Political ghost causing some hilarity (5,6)

DOWN

1 Superior show of anger to ensure one soon gets the post (5-5,5)
2 Coal distributed before taking a break for a drink (7)
3 Creates a stink when leader deserts Europeans (5)
4 Music-maker's tale of leg show that's different (9)
5 Susceptible to being a matter for discussion (7)
6 Be relaxed about shirt not tucked in (3,2,3,4,3)
7 Mark of some careless person's mud generously spread (6)
8 Occasion when a man becomes a servant (6)
16 Craft offering fish a way in (9)
18 Enthusiastic study requiring all-round skill (6)
19 A person in support could show the way (7)
21 One has no aim to cause a split in revolutionary rising (7)
23 One doesn't go straight ahead as an artist (6)
25 Don't go round the ring in a bad posture (5)

11

ACROSS

1 Apple produced the Spanish seaside way (7)
5 Talk of having to be back in time (6)
9 Had been expected to leave for a drinking party (7)
10 Touch a girl on the knee (7)
11 Position that is achieved after half a century (3)
12 One provides the wind that makes a vessel appear (5-6)
13 Old man of Rome (5)
14 Lemon trap set by American cops (9)
16 One demonstrating support for a trial (9)
17 Fear of a coiled adder (5)
19 Al tangles with saucy Lois in bawdy style (11)
22 Member of a jolly lot (3)
23 Plant everything and get better (7)
24 Snubbed girl possibly a killer (7)
26 Native in bed taken out to eat (6)
27 Not the usual way to get to the mountains (7)

DOWN

1 Plant in front of animal's tongue (7)
2 Have no great hopes of a theatre outing when a body's found (7,4,4)
3 A sporting occasion without me as head man (3)
4 She's been sick on the way up (5)
5 Poised to turn right on the way to the bank maybe (9)
6 Some sort of nut might be on the phone shortly (5)
7 Auf wiedersehen, English! (4,2,4,5)
8 Respectable woman going mad on tram (6)
12 Last of the fingerprints found in blood could be a plant (5)
14 Given a drug one raises the temperature in the hope of making money (3-6)
15 Not even this style is revealing in a strange way (5)
16 As a philosopher you have imbibed a little science, friend! (6)
18 The estate needs me to sort it out (7)
20 Caught all the others on top (5)
21 Blows on one's feet (5)
25 Jack's desert get-up (3)

ACROSS

1 Another opportunity to support a gamble (6,6)
8 One may be provisionally licensed to take instruction (7)
9 Light scheme not starting to get the bird (7)
11 No consuming anger when the cane is employed (10)
12 Get together in a quiet manner (4)
14 Died of cold? (8)
16 Stick had to be broken before (6)
17 Be pictured as having no standing (3)
19 Movement forward needed after first part of play (6)
21 Country leadership in some sort of harmony as a rule (8)
24 Awfully bad bit of play (4)
25 Uncensored talk about liberty (4,6)
27 Take back what you said about the land (7)
28 Word for word involvement (7)
29 Growth being good for what ails (6,6)

DOWN

1 Keep starting to speak (7)
2 Deceptive account of getting religion (10)
3 Tells how to arrange a Scottish island get-up (8)
4 State one business that could be material (6)
5 Little Lord Fauntleroy's relation (4)
6 Burn me up in a box (7)
7 The whole musical audience indicating the game's not decided (3,2,4,3)
10 Young versery (7,5)
13 A spot of perfection (5,5)
15 Not very clever rise in the centre (3)
18 Allow real fiddling in a betting system (8)
20 Peg conceals corruption in a member of a board (7)
22 Cell emptied in good time as you can see (7)
23 It's cruel to rub out most of the story (6)
26 Spike finds where the drinks are and starts on the beer (4)

13

ACROSS

6 Work of failed artist given to paper people (9,5)
9 One hopes those in the swim will come for a bite (6)
10 Quiet song account for dramatic announcement (8)
11 People who hope to make savings (8)
13 Bully for him! (6)
15 Hornet flying round high place (6)
17 Guidance as to what's wrong with sales material (6)
19 Bitterness continuing in some measure (6)
20 Clergyman given tea without frills (8)
22 One's learning to put a little chap right on the other side (8)
24 Lots of people rejoice when the Social Democrats are returned (6)
26 A nice new point made by the politician here a long time ago (7,7)

DOWN

1 Hand me a lantern so we can see the old chap (11,3)
2 Determination to make late dispositions (4)
3 The way things are going at college (6)
4 White effect achieved by having drawn blood from every one inside (8)
5 Objections raised at the end (4)
7 Set poems out after one (6)
8 Have a bad time when a person takes five daily breaks in Niagara (4,2,4,4)
12 Some sort of island king taking fuel round (5)
14 Get cold at church when under the weather (5)
16 It fails to happen when there are no people at the opening (3-5)
18 Be quick to apply heat (6)
21 Charge card capturing no man's custom (6)
23 Attack the other end to bring help (4)
25 Smell arising with Old Etonian in the orchestra (4)

14

ACROSS

1 Firm conclusion that this part does the work (8,3)
9 Dog among children made safe (7)
10 Used to provide enough illustration (7)
11 I shall shortly be sick! (3)
12 One may be expected to make a cross choice (7)
13 Dutch leader is having to run back and do the twist (7)
14 One thing and another (3)
15 Coffee when there's little time for tea (5)
17 Record your brief help on the way back (5)
18 What one might get from a sap concerning bad behaviour (5)
20 Deal with menace without getting hot (5)
22 Little chap one found to be representative (3)
24 Decisive state in which police in Belfast find one (7)
25 Polish one has to study as an important line to cross (7)
26 Half 14 (3)
27 Night on the razzle without object (7)
28 Material with size to accommodate two males (7)
29 Damaging a strong sole could be a minor misfortune (2,5,4)

DOWN

1 Horticultural graduates continue to use their heads (9,6)
2 Soldiers among fools standing up on the level (7)
3 Drain out at the lowest point (5)
4 Endlessly bombard Admiral Bird (9)
5 Went by mistake into editorial leaders (7)
6 Dead ambassador finally left out when a representative group is formed (10,5)
7 Agreement obtained when given an errand (6)
8 Someone to guard the southern gate (6)
16 List animal making a record turn to the East (9)
18 Repudiate regular payment including a bill that turns up (6)
19 Point where the sick need action that gives a fix (7)
21 Explorer coming up with firm offer of crop to be burnt (7)
23 Heavily criticise an old lady in hat (6)
25 Argue against raising potato (5)

ACROSS

1 Inspired one to go in when soldiers leave the weak (7)
5 Put right only after he left the chief (6)
9 Make cuts in what's possibly not hers (7)
10 One gives instruction for the race to be fixed (7)
11 The new arrival may break out of it (3)
12 Captures style in a building block (11)
13 Not very clever to be in the gardens every night (5)
14 Monty and Irma might get together in it (9)
16 Sensible cloth floor covering you'll see in the illustration shortly (9)
17 Swimmer in a fur coat (5)
19 Cap Harry got given for ingeniously drawing plans (11)
22 One may look wise in a respectable bowler hat (3)
23 Characters inclined to suggest special importance (7)
24 Near enough to be seen to have perception (7)
26 Prince seen to mingle with Alcoholics Anonymous (6)
27 Used former spouse to chop tree until dead (7)

DOWN

1 Accepted squashed dates as a substitute (7)
2 What might give a girl a double-barrelled name? (7,8)
3 One loved to be in a huff (3)
4 One has a consuming interest in colour being put up outside (5)
5 Genuine university article in grotesque surroundings (9)
6 That girl's got her legs covered (5)
7 Where you learn to use your head teaching (6,2,7)
8 Where blood flows in the road (6)
12 What's best about the paper (5)
14 People of drive (9)
15 Woman hiding gold tooth (5)
16 Choose the old devil for sound eating out (6)
18 Having some connection with what's been told (7)
20 She has nothing but will survive (5)
21 Exercises about to free lions (5)
25 She is separated from the children (3)

8

... crossword grid ...

(7)

... without getting caught in the cross-fire (8)

... Italian food but a bit of a hindrance (2,5)

... on a blue flower with due (6)

... couple of these (3)

... in a lying position (4)

26. Damage due to leap in profitability, not (6)

27. Working on a connection with used aircraft fuel (7)

28. The lines need a stir, initially (4,3)

29. Expresses satire on the stage (4)

30. Short, separated from everything (5)

16

ACROSS

1 Shop money? Take it away! (4,3,5)
8 Economy advice having no effect (7)
9 Characteristic gold offer by renegade (7)
11 Move by not quite stupid and coy cold-style supporter (6,4)
12 Don't start extra payment for responsibility (4)
14 Some sort of heel attaining eminence in cards (8)
16 Villain captured by spies seen to be one that's very small (6)
17 Money may be a problem for children (3)
19 Not quite a leading Labour majority (6)
21 Newly identified a penny in the distribution of debits (8)
24 She can make a comeback all the same (4)
25 More uncovered on the run that doesn't make sense (10)
27 Remain baffled by the river when one's used to the sea (7)
28 Uproar in court maybe (7)
29 Nylong? (7,5)

DOWN

1 Not an honest sound animal (7)
2 Expert at mixing spice with a number of items (10)
3 Relieves the fools protecting the university silver (8)
4 Take away the cad that's done wrong (6)
5 He'll make you lose your head, my lady! (4)
6 Ring for the plan of the building (7)
7 It may make one afraid to take things away (7,5)
10 Call to adopt a bright get-up (4,3,5)
13 A choir list possibly going back a long way (10)
15 Payment made to raise transport (3)
18 Fruity bureaucrat (8)
20 High pointer for Arabs who are in the money (7)
22 Stop somewhere along the line (7)
23 Shortage of fabulously rich stuff (6)
26 Supporter of an appeal to highest authority (4)

ACROSS

6 Stay here to get a partnership started (9,5)
9 Game block concealing one's identity (6)
10 Face time on the promenade (8)
11 Ring representative in the plant to apply a squeeze (8)
13 Person of religion being a bit of a mug will lose pounds (6)
15 Rig act to look very sad (6)
17 Where the beastly may get food in a depression (6)
19 Came across a carrier able to show the way (6)
20 Wonder expressed at finding a suitable place for the coast road (8)
22 Talk of what's appropriate about one achieving a record (8)
24 Perceive to be out of this world (6)
26 Supplier of no personality (7,7)

DOWN

1 Cast hoping to produce a successful number (5,2,3,4)
2 Not favouring wine that hasn't got a lot of chic (4)
3 Close to having departed and been forgotten (6)
4 One makes a telling contribution to police work (8)
5 Kick the car at last (4)
7 Ring a swimmer of limited intelligence (6)
8 Language as a means of communication between countries (7,7)
12 Steal away to cook eggs (5)
14 Initially seen as unilaterally declaring independence of Arabia (5)
16 Poor Asian man lacking an article (8)
18 Show not how best to express pain (6)
21 Cut down and turn into corrupt creed (6)
23 Where swimmers circulate under cover (4)
25 Conceited one in a leading position (4)

ACROSS

1 Does wrong and after a time is ruined (8)
5 Student gathering place affected by America (6)
9 She achieved promotion with army manoeuvres (8)
10 Critic in trouble for being acid (6)
12 One gets round to making a point (4)
13 Nice meal or break with formality (10)
15 Fill a wood fracture? When a man's around she has to do everything! (4,2,3,4)
19 In a good position to make an attractive picture (7,6)
23 Work to get a runner back on the river where there's entertainment (5,5)
25 Compelling reason for thinking Jumbo's in a frenzy (4)
28 This way to the centre (6)
29 Split in the army (8)
30 Have a success with the girl this way (6)
31 Bound to make money in unusual deeds (8)

DOWN

1 Show the way to be straight (6)
2 She makes light of possessing female attraction (5)
3 Outstanding collection of self-employed building workers (4)
4 Sink to start running awful dope (7)
6 Find a way to move a foreign friend (5)
7 Being tight or may spin round (9)
8 Similar to being of a kind to approve (8)
11 Goddess of the rain forest (4)
14 She can take off without being caught (4)
15 Test the lady's repartee – it's only common sense! (6-3)
16 No success – losing money – that's dandy! (3)
17 Dead slow in arriving (4)
18 Cause surprise when ash is not removed (8)
20 Continue to appear a fool (4)
21 Break needed where malevolence is concerned (7)
22 Having got high the hard way? (6)
24 Allow to change gear at the end of the lane (5)
26 Getting together for service without the commander getting a medal (5)
27 It's sweet to make a lot of money (4)

19

ACROSS

1 Recording that won't let go? Stick with it (8,4)
8 Cause anger with a perfume (7)
9 Almost certain there'll be more left over (7)
11 One country boy put inside for telling (10)
12 Bender one might go on to make an appeal (4)
14 Records new way to make the rich save (8)
16 Quarter allocated for hut to be built (6)
17 Uncovered in depth (3)
19 One feels the pull of America (6)
21 They may get immersed in religion (8)
24 Lily offers a drink (4)
25 Reckoning on being able to give a reason (10)
27 One seems to have no aim but to go fishing (7)
28 Dense growth of the stupid and foreign (7)
29 Drink made with fruit by putting foreign money in (6,6)

DOWN

1 Ice cast out in a spirit of self-denial (7)
2 Manicurist at one's service? (10)
3 Put some warmth in the outhouse just in case (8)
4 Seeing victory one is turned on (6)
5 Not a good girl perhaps but sharp (4)
6 Awful perils about the way you take foreign beer (7)
7 It may give soldiers sound encouragement (8,4)
10 Get very angry over the prospects of what tourists will do (3,3,6)
13 Argument about what's inside one with rising disagreement (10)
15 Transport set-up for one going beneath the surface shortly (3)
18 He'll kill little Georgia, the cad! (8)
20 Encourage in hours of difficulty (7)
22 Clever to conceal speed in such a deft way (7)
23 Sexy at first and attractively shaped but suffering from lack of vitamin C (6)
26 Give top performance in a most artistic dance routine (4)

ACROSS

1 Agreement on record to provide music maybe (7,4)
9 Killer standing on the wrong road (7)
10 Going for a ride one might put one's foot in it (7)
11 Fire saint who won't go round a tree (3)
12 One's learned to mark an inner break (7)
13 Being stupid is a fault in the East (7)
14 Put on a party beginning now! (3)
15 One teaches how to dock an animal's tail (5)
17 Drink takes a long time going from one side to the other (5)
18 First chance to see the light (3-2)
20 One with something to confess? (5)
22 Deposit money with a hundred deducted (3)
24 One may descend safely after pulling it (3-4)
25 Rough lads can give offence (7)
26 Fool getting up in a tree (3)
27 Being unpleasant is accepted to be smart all round (7)
28 Graceful support shown in neat manoeuvre (7)
29 Someone else signs for his spirited work (5-6)

DOWN

1 Arrest a tipster who isn't alert? (5,3,7)
2 Elder doctor around who can't stop interfering (7)
3 Name the river where you can dry clothes (5)
4 The way madness within the town limits an islander (9)
5 First character to give some idea of identity (7)
6 More than one drawing of old transport (8,3,4)
7 I am accustomed to be offered entertainment (6)
8 Seen to be a very quiet listener (6)
16 Dandy killed for giving an inflamed look (9)
18 Hassle the other woman – no way! (6)
19 Reservation in favour of a small girl like this (7)
21 Chemical test substance given a ripping time inside (7)
23 The man is given a great deal by the slaves (6)
25 Point of attack (5)

ACROSS

1 Part for instance with people in the street (7)
5 Worries finally doubled at a stroke (6)
9 She's got another girl to take on Eve's boy (7)
10 Insignificant man wrestling with lion (7)
11 Forgive Don for dropping standard (3)
12 See it sounds out to boring effect (11)
13 Person at the top to keep things straight (5)
14 Tried for catches around the vessel provided (9)
16 Chewed core in a dish could drip (9)
17 Lobby for you to be admitted (5)
19 Bet you'll have a series of wins (11)
22 There might be some point to taking it (3)
23 Man absorbing nothing taken aback by one in Africa (7)
24 Like being depressed when parted (7)
26 Go into it for a break (6)
27 Supporter of the board (7)

DOWN

1 Run second settlement for the Queen (7)
2 Training the top brass in relief of suffering? (7,8)
3 Go out after achieving a high (3)
4 Faced with idle drifting after starting time (5)
5 Space to study the race situation (9)
6 Roman twin about to raise a problem (5)
7 From a remote point in time (5,3,4,3)
8 Shut up or be unsuccessful in recording (6)
12 The trunk may be left in the janitor's office (5)
14 Start finding permanent way links have weak points (9)
15 Presume to be unproductive when a tile is missing (5)
16 Statement of grievance by one in the factory (6)
18 Feeling of guilt where the code is concerned (7)
20 Animal having some trouble going round the ring (5)
21 Here's health to a good chap! (5)
25 Computer operator having no time for employment (3)

ACROSS

1 They come down before May's bloomers are seen (5,7)
8 Out in a cab without Jack to arrange a sale (7)
9 Help the rest to turn a vehicle (7)
11 Old man taken to dance as Mum's new partner (10)
12 Go round delivering a blow (4)
14 Dad's attempts at providing something for tea (8)
16 Expert not moving at once (6)
17 Find it agreeable to shut one's eyes (3)
19 Group not admitted at the beginning (6)
21 Could be gained in law – Ben's seen a new way (8)
24 Firm being cruel (4)
25 Cancel tea arranged by someone not feeling well (10)
27 Plant where production may be down (7)
28 Send without starting to make movement (7)
29 Difficult issue – one's in need of guidance (7,5)

DOWN

1 Old shooters could be responsible for her scar (7)
2 Control made it necessary to be given more strength (10)
3 Extend disturbance in the glen after that (8)
4 Possesses the number needed to speed things up (6)
5 Some sort of gear for a low wretch (4)
6 Get in a new row when genuine gin is served out (7)
7 Things don't happen as one predicts (5,7)
10 Series of happenings when the water rises? (4,2,6)
13 Ring if a pan is needed for making plant (10)
15 This way to the first winter broadcast (3)
18 Performed first part of play before being caught moralising (8)
20 A dog could stray into a bank (7)
22 Air-beds given hot treatment (7)
23 Bless you for that small outburst! (6)
26 Fliers rise to inflict injury (4)

ACROSS

6 Ready to fire with intent to force admission? (6,8)
9 Save just a little butter? (6)
10 No end of fine twirling around in it! (8)
11 Exciting drink producing an involuntary movement (8)
13 Flexible bridge? (6)
15 The attractions of sabotage in the Civil Service (6)
17 Show to be in charge in a small part of the store (6)
19 Spread objection to the central mysteries (6)
20 Unable to return first service covering the line given (8)
22 There's a lot of laughter in all that needling (8)
24 Too much crosses the sound, you might say (6)
26 There could be trouble for the head's supporter at this rate (9,5)

DOWN

1 Current use of pluck to create harmony (8,6)
2 A prisoner turns up for the festivity (4)
3 Change sides when you find something wrong (6)
4 Unavoidably producing trouble for creep (8)
5 Take some of these to new school (4)
7 One of a number of same-day arrivals given church fruit (6)
8 Over there among opponents (2,3,5,4)
12 Intended to be malicious first time (5)
14 Cheese needing the right plant (5)
16 One who sells a foreign sea song (8)
18 Doesn't allow bill to be presented for wine (6)
21 Line about to be accepted by the cabinet (6)
23 Take up a role that allows no escape (4)
25 Sounded very pleased to be in company (4)

24

ACROSS

1 Fifty per cent return on the side (4-4)
5 Line the woman saw tangled inside (6)
9 Move to the right in the way a moral tale is told (8)
10 Work back into new draught (6)
12 Give approval to late payment (4)
13 Have canals diverted into falls (10)
15 Where to dry out when drinking with the management (8-5)
19 The stock market fans the flames when people fight (8,5)
23 Promise Nato big oil deal (10)
25 Animal shut up (4)
28 Get back with Georgia in control (6)
29 Reject what's wrongly said to take the pound down (8)
30 Go terribly green and yellow at first (6)
31 German ship arrived at the end of four months (8)

DOWN

1 Listen to empty tosh in front of the fire (6)
2 Colour one goes in when a visit is set up (5)
3 More than enough luggage (4)
4 Where one's at home as a traveller (7)
6 What makes one's standing painful might lead to growth (5)
7 Youths to uncover top people (9)
8 Where strikes can be closely observed (8)
11 Clearly seen to drop one scheme (4)
14 Hit a priest (4)
15 Notes sign containing a record of commandments (9)
16 Sack without loud anger (3)
17 Reserve in some volume (4)
18 Ingenuity about where the leak comes from (8)
20 Samuel's place – you can't tell when you're there (4)
21 Doctor held up when newly-wed comes round for a sedative (7)
22 Cream off finally at a reduced level (6)
24 State of the course on the move (5)
26 She's engaged in a novel-length work of imagination (5)
27 Where shopping is worth a lot to everyone (4)

25

ACROSS

1 Leader promising endurance all the way (5,2,4)
9 Garment covering water container (4,3)
10 Fax diverted into growth that doesn't benefit the Government (3-4)
11 Those confused people, they're all at it (3)
12 Any fast move may be just invention (7)
13 Creeps into the trees identifying girl as being missing (7)
14 Name the last person coming from Bengal (3)
15 Small and delicate fish heading into river the wrong way (5)
17 Hate to express contempt to the English (5)
18 Stuff a pound into broken lute (5)
20 Otherwise you have to cut the deck (5)
22 Transport message with part left off (3)
24 It provides cover for fighters all the same (7)
25 Trail round the ends of the earth to find a patron (7)
26 Breaking the law enables one to get through (3)
27 Start to bring trouble to Zaire where there could be a flare-up (7)
28 Enthusiastic reception featuring eggs? (7)
29 Feed that's no treat, one could say with a smile (5,6)

DOWN

1 It's magical what one can do with money! (9,6)
2 Desert people in a scramble to get on (3,4)
3 Hints you're starting to have too much to drink (5)
4 Shape of coat to be changed before you move along (9)
5 Concerned person losing head and getting cross over debts (7)
6 Jacket, waistcoat, trousers and a bit extra to sit on (5-5,5)
7 Pole taking central place in the Hebrides (6)
8 One has time for an occupation (6)
16 Creature given time to move unceremoniously (4-5)
18 They could be down for lack of approval (6)
19 One admires oneself for having obtained a winning position after an excellent start (7)
21 It shows one has a will to execute (7)
23 Going through without interest (6)
25 Opening with a head start? Nothing doing! (5)

2 Home or residence in ancient country (5) (3)
3 The response to a question there is no point (4)
5 Force you to submit, overwhelm power to resist (5)
6 Bid, a threat to pre-eminence, before you demonstrate (9) (?)
and 5 Reorganised so as to switch a signal getting cross over
to embrace, gets stricter (9) (?) (3, 4, 2, 5)
4 Jockey, sporting that race, needed to ensure sit on? (3, 7, 3)
7 Probing certain datering - by this he do... (6)
10 One has time for attention (4)
15 Feature given firm's approval interminably (?)
21 They could be down for lack of approval (?)
19 Quandaries one owner may have increased a winning person
should be excellent, nearly (?)
23 If a move one may will to rescue (7)
24 Amazing, turning a block in excess (6)
26 Country with a large sea, disturbing doubt (5)

ACROSS

1 The person after Pat may be? (7)
5 Cut out in obscure cover, it's said (6)
9 Cunning social ends gained by people having a row (7)
10 Lulu's of a different persuasion expressing deep feelings (7)
11 Deposit on land without rock (3)
12 Animal able to deliver kicks of an entertaining character? (4,2,5)
13 More tax involving the Queen (5)
14 The woman with records related to leather (9)
16 Mend a torn, crumpled decoration (9)
17 One up (5)
19 One might be taken in this way (11)
22 Governor taking a day off when there's a strike (3)
23 Hide caught on lace ruffle (7)
24 Take over from a lady after about half a life (7)
26 Form of writing for an author to attempt (6)
27 Goes round to stare rudely (7)

DOWN

1 Spend a long time on the way there (7)
2 Examine action options when help is requested (3,4,3,3,2)
3 The face of a fool (3)
4 Intent on getting a rise in money (5)
5 Is a man in depression becoming a rebel? (9)
6 Not much left after you've cut a slice (5)
7 One can't continue with services when dress is lacking (9,6)
8 She's given a bit of a line by the boy (6)
12 See one on board about the right sea food (5)
14 Silly pace modified in a particular way (9)
15 Block line after a knock-up (5)
16 Produce one more to be taken to court as being on drugs (6)
18 Hold back where the papers are concerned (7)
20 Fold a broken petal (5)
21 Something wrong with trial maybe (5)
25 Bible man's fortune (3)

ACROSS

1 Wrong letter sent about me being put down somewhere else (12)
8 Sounds an odd time to make a search (7)
9 Gem dealer craftily hiding first of many (7)
11 Moving experience of the Twenties (7,3)
12 Growth in a hot atmosphere (4)
14 Scores of links, departed included (8)
16 Will says you've got it coming to you (6)
17 Skirting? Not round the old fellow (3)
19 Having power that could get you started (6)
21 Act as substitute for tepid use of reorganisation (8)
24 Article we have to return for fresh use (4)
25 Let down an applicant for a job? (10)
27 If less is to be distributed have to start looking after No 1 (7)
28 State where terrorists go in to meet trouble (7)
29 Quality one can't do with (12)

DOWN

1 Love to introduce Papist to the Church of England (7)
2 It's a cattle hazard hanging from the roof (10)
3 Felt unsteady and on edge maybe (8)
4 Set out to take in a small rise in latitude (6)
5 Suitable gathering for a pursuit (4)
6 Turn once more before the artist falls (7)
7 Soldier's pay releasing one from earning a living? (7,5)
10 Conditions outside not permitting a clean-up (5,7)
13 Umpires not prepared to allow a new start (10)
15 Not happy with the endless run-up (3)
18 Immoral impression given when rebel Jack comes in (8)
20 Linger uncertainly around men's leader thought to be a trouble-maker (7)
22 Take off one on the way to the pictures (7)
23 Being a churchman one can't go straight ahead on board (6)
26 Outfit held up by nothing but a benefit cheque maybe (4)

28

ACROSS

6 Make a girl turn to give a fiery display (9,5)
9 Record backing in simple colour (6)
10 Treat badly in having to hurry for praise (8)
11 One might bring warmth into a home (8)
13 Steal money given to start education (6)
15 Meaning to bring something from abroad (6)
17 Introduce a composer needing a bit of room inside (6)
19 Training meant to make a pupil intellectual (6)
20 Give the lady the thing that takes time to become a tradition (8)
22 Something to wear in Wales (8)
24 As to being in public relations, he can offer a service (6)
26 Assurance of having one's own personality (4-10)

DOWN

1 Grammarian's luggage suggesting guilt? (10,4)
2 Lots of money coming up – don't let it go further! (4)
3 Previously shown programme about fuel (6)
4 Bottle unable to be swallowed by an animal (8)
5 Attempt at getting killed (4)
7 Popular business not doing well (6)
8 Listener approaching those crushed so as to know what's going on (3,2,3,6)
12 What's needed before there can be any outcome (5)
14 Put down in the works (5)
16 Half a life spent in an area of worship (8)
18 Complains about his new disposition (6)
21 Commemorative meal? (6)
23 Clever French here abandon loss (4)
25 Go over the snow to the top of a mountain and glide along the surface (4)

29

ACROSS

1 It's characteristic of the Princess to be absent-minded (8)
5 Moving at the same pace on foot (6)
9 Show round a small island heaven (8)
10 Name a journalist finds a drawback (6)
12 Flat in a house of the Venetian style (4)
13 Taking one thing with another, is there a resemblance? (10)
15 People liked to be seen approving a proposition (5,2,6)
19 Work nearly great – it has someone to see it (8,5)
23 The crew fiddle daily, not first-class but in a bad way (10)
25 One goes on foot right away from the coast (4)
28 What we have to perform inside stinks! (6)
29 Nice beef chopped up for a living (8)
30 It's a bit much – lies around at breakfast! (6)
31 Turn in a sailor, don't to around giving figures (8)

DOWN

1 Smart enough to start daily paper round (6)
2 Material from one of the lesser German literary works (5)
3 Have a leg on each side? Best not if you want to get a horse going (4)
4 Coming as part of the retail trade (2,5)
6 Drain faulty at the lowest point (5)
7 Rapture that may have one carried away (9)
8 Be curious about Dante's awful quibbling (8)
11 Go over one's life (4)
14 Dreary party at the old place (4)
15 King's part in Lear, for one (5,4)
16 One very small girl (3)
17 We agree to make changes without coming to a conclusion (4)
18 One makes light of being such a small creature (4-4)
20 One of the birds overhead can't fly! (4)
21 Complaint of bends in metal (7)
22 Well-known person a bit lacking when encountered in one's salad days (6)
24 Old skeletons can be found right in the coal (5)
26 Bit of a laugh if anything starts in Israel (5)
27 Happening not beginning to be something of a let-out (4)

ACROSS

1 One who likes a flutter? (4-7)
9 Carry out and kill (7)
10 Royal house chair (7)
11 Help to drop first animal (3)
12 Line in front of vessel as navigation aid (7)
13 Cover animal taking line back inside (7)
14 Agree to move the head (3)
15 Lovable creature in the wrong bib this morning (5)
17 Loved to be a party man (5)
18 Endless casket-shaking to find things to eat (5)
20 Say what could be true – about time! (5)
22 Make a point of giving advice (3)
24 Sketch an escape route (7)
25 Application to turn animal back when the tune changes (7)
26 Brown man leaving a line out of the circle (3)
27 The dog that's right for a miner (7)
28 Accommodation that's over the top in prison (7)
29 His work may reach a very high point (11)

DOWN

1 Idle enjoyment of what's knocked back with those knocked over (4,3,8)
2 Stage crowd talk of what may be cooking (7)
3 Fare badly and begin to be kinky strange one (5)
4 It provides a basis for daily reading (9)
5 Grid one might be seen not to have recognised (7)
6 Having a fun companion get up early (4,4,3,4)
7 Figure presented by a boy (6)
8 Cold without moving off the end first (6)
16 Get doctor to employ a raised bit that could mean death to the timid (9)
18 Duck in an Essex river (6)
19 Dispatch by oneself (7)
21 Great muddle over volunteers causing a lot of rows maybe (7)
23 One's able to make vessels move idly about (6)
25 One in the family who might take the pledge (5)

ACROSS

1 Explode when given stale stuff for a snack (7)
5 Art objects eventually beginning to show quality (6)
9 Make neat pushes back before a number (7)
10 It's very good for a Christmas pull (7)
11 Insect right off drink (3)
12 One doesn't like people to find mother's pain unusual (11)
13 Such a large number must be obscene! (5)
14 Eve racing around to make a complaint (9)
16 Puts off concealing aim to get people to fight back (9)
17 One as good as another (5)
19 It's right to remedy the head's mistake (11)
22 One that's cracked going round to get tight (3)
23 One might give you a false smile (7)
24 Slightly disreputable swimmer following fliers (7)
26 Some simple verses that may get things moving (6)
27 Went off to trap you in a high-class fiddle (7)

DOWN

1 Letters received after a shooting (7)
2 Talk about the end of the war (5,10)
3 Choose work at the last moment (3)
4 Dressing up numbers (5)
5 Openings one's found among holidays in France (9)
6 Accessible stretch of river (5)
7 How many have failed to make a name? (7,8)
8 Get wind of some sort of block (6)
12 Person thus included as a member of society (5)
14 Distinction achieved perhaps as Regents (9)
15 Has a look at the opinions expressed (5)
16 Make clear if there's fish in the river (6)
18 Made fast new chat when being taken around (7)
20 Get away from the Spanish due to a diversion (5)
21 Makes money as a receiver of speeches to the Poles (5)
25 Priest having to conceal high-class coat (3)

ACROSS

1 How quickly punishment is administered? (8,4)
8 Attempts to get the players a morning off in port (7)
9 One thinks one needs them all – for a game maybe (7)
11 Brown gives thanks for a horse – or what's very similar (10)
12 Give a hand all round (4)
14 Second agreement about a call for sprays (8)
16 Nerve needed to hold a lot of drink (6)
17 The rule in India is to return a drink (3)
19 Longs to spend time with the Poles (6)
21 Trains Welsh to prevent falling off a ship (8)
24 Money for getting the blame passed? (4)
25 Spaniard in a USA land deal (10)
27 Bill felt different on the grass (7)
28 Business worry (7)
29 Met in sin romp that has brought about retribution (12)

DOWN

1 One might take a turn at bowling (7)
2 Jack may be making his mark by not voting (10)
3 Collapse like a vegetable up on top (4,4)
4 Complain about the short time devoted to awarding a title (6)
5 Drink at the end of the voyage (4)
6 Gather to offer prayer (7)
7 It shows you've got somewhere in society (6,6)
10 More pleasant side of a clouded situation (6,6)
13 Study way of escape when one leaves nice meeting (10)
15 Faced an artist for a day (3)
18 Crowd first-rate vessel from an island (8)
20 Back in the centre to demand honour (7)
22 It sustains one in mental turmoil (7)
23 Makes one see the tune is to be rewritten (6)
26 It's not clear what's left in the polish-up (4)

ACROSS

6 Able to go for a rise (8,6)
9 Has something to say in America (6)
10 They may be in the food you can get from one strip (8)
11 Tea with Carol possibly a matter of some heat (8)
13 Shocked to find something puzzling in a publicity item (6)
15 Works the other way when you employ your partner (6)
17 Sign for a star couple (6)
19 A lot of lies in the paper? (6)
20 People not starting to face fancy (8)
22 Discernible in a stammering person with children (8)
24 Give one a gun after fifty if you want to get the message (6)
26 Not much consolation after breaking bread (5,2,7)

DOWN

1 Game to look for one going on foot (4,3,7)
2 Pulls up for intensive study (4)
3 Hey, it's happening all at once! (6)
4 Give wretched Tim a mole to sacrifice (8)
5 Fit to be left in Lincoln (4)
7 They turn over on the personal front (6)
8 Hanging around can be fatal (9,5)
12 Dance of a sort round a ring shows where one comes from (5)
14 A canvas sent up in another name (5)
16 Where lessons are given after breaking elks' bones (8)
18 Tip out in a very short time if poisoned (6)
21 The quantity brought to book (6)
23 Head off crazy fighters (4)
25 Give a demonstration of the way to follow a bend in the road (4)

ACROSS

1 Grand joke with the one in the raincoat (8)
5 Takes steps to start a census among foreigners (6)
9 Reduce size by agreement (8)
10 One flies to get a short-time view of the world (6)
12 Otherwise having to return some of one's letters (4)
13 Don't provide enough dilution in depth (10)
15 Things happening now could be shocking, it seems (7,6)
19 Always trying to attract attention by top treatment (9,4)
23 Quite hot perhaps in an uncultured style (10)
25 Get out of shape for fighting the onset of poverty (4)
28 Language used by the sailor with one in a car crash (6)
29 Took action about fur for the physically challenged (8)
30 Awful threat by a top provider (6)
31 Apply a rag to it or one might make trouble (8)

DOWN

1 Proverbial wine one doesn't take seriously (6)
2 A family to keep up with (5)
3 Ride on waves of Internet information? (4)
4 Madden with perfume (7)
6 Let everybody express pain (5)
7 Study the position of a lake (9)
8 One sends up a girl to central casting after she's had a picture taken (8)
11 Exploit part of what's unsafe at times (4)
14 Extent of sunken space (4)
15 One goes in for fish, underground plant stem or insect (9)
16 The word lacks nothing when one's religious (3)
17 Show the sappers out for something to eat (4)
18 See money is paid when you've got a deal (4,4)
20 Therefore let the frightener stand up! (4)
21 Effective in narration (7)
22 Creature starting to show pride of a sort (6)
24 Give a view all round a tree (5)
26 Share out in what sounds a good deal (5)
27 Thrown into play (4)

ACROSS

1 All of you associate form with music (4,3,4)
9 Have to get a taxi back when you've business in the Smoke (7)
10 Superior Eastern lady providing the fruit (7)
11 Not a standard bird – rubbish (3)
12 He gets around a lot of regular drinkers (7)
13 They may be needed for a put-up job (7)
14 Resort perhaps finally suffering a setback (3)
15 Favoured girl allowed to embrace the monarch (5)
17 Record help needed to get back on line (5)
18 See the chaplain before including an announcement (5)
20 Signal a stoppage after it turns in need of a rest (5)
22 Drops on the grass (3)
24 Appeal in connection with a mission (7)
25 Awful kid's lie causes hostility (7)
26 Putting one's in could be interfering (3)
27 There's little in the gun that means to pacify (7)
28 One more unknown member of the team (7)
29 Spaniel with obtrusive head? (4,7)

DOWN

1 Fantasy with pipe fry-up (6-3-6)
2 Claimed to have difficulty seeing the point (7)
3 Deck trouble with sailors (5)
4 Warship man in Desert Storm (9)
5 Forced to be thankful (7)
6 Miracle diet for the multitude (6,3,6)
7 Gives an impression of bad temper (6)
8 Wet planet becoming heavy shortly (6)
16 Give the pet a stimulant when in some sort of trance (9)
18 It's the vicar's responsibility to knock up his erring characters (6)
19 Not getting a rise after always playing football (7)
21 Do piles of damage (7)
23 Go wrong in questioning the reason for a craft (6)
25 Play the healer and become a master (5)

CRITICAL...

crossword clues

Going where an actor goes (7,3)
People's CDS for on the understudy (9)
Voice that gets passed about by a nosy Parker (9,4)
Specious and dangerously speculative?
Very fundamental... one reason? (5)
...works when brewing? Me, work (4,4) (6)
Nine, not upon a subject... gone in less time of waiting (5)
It supports our department on the make up the world (3)
...in the form (5)
He gets nobby a deserter... always letting roll in ball)
Monument of distinction; and move it freely into a column (7)
For a song in question... he is ready for actual (5)
...I don't his heart and homey's contrary try... time (9
...small... but... picture of a door at a doorstep (9)
It snorts as an escape for money

36

ACROSS

1 They provide support for those retiring (7)
5 Quite good at avoiding immodesty (6)
9 A fool who conceals bad behaviour can be laughed at (7)
10 Height figure being about right (7)
11 Add up what you might drink (3)
12 Shaky tables one let fall when set up (11)
13 Wager about going in for personal cover (5)
14 Quick to see where cuts might be made? (5-4)
16 Lets grand composition be suppressed (9)
17 Show the way to mark a stop (5)
19 Wavy stripe on vessel denoting church's worldly ambition (11)
22 Little chap given money a penny short (3)
23 A retired boxer, among others, has no illusions (7)
24 Away with the team where there's not much of a chance? (7)
26 Wonder if Proust could be edited (6)
27 Forgetting men are different in the East (7)

DOWN

1 The thinker drops one but gets a rise for hidden gifts here (4-3)
2 Annoying shopkeeper providing a vexatious replacement (7-8)
3 Somewhat indelicate priest (3)
4 Glimpse of a blot on the landscape (5)
5 Be quick to give management a display of instruments (9)
6 Creature one has come to cover (5)
7 How bad times were a century ago! (7,8)
8 Inclined to need to be given care (6)
12 Sent to the interior of East Africa to catch up (5)
14 Reorganising its oil company requires the right lawyer (9)
15 Doubly self-righteous Tory starts to get the bird (5)
16 The very good second-rate can be wonderful (6)
18 Turn up overweight and suffer awful fate of a material sort (7)
20 Go quickly over the money and provide very little (5)
21 Scent the shortcoming of a capital fellow (5)
25 Don't spoil a man for money (3)

37

ACROSS

1 One might be put out by taking it in (8,4)
8 Crazy instinct to take ten before moving a muscle (7)
9 Harry is more distressed in an explosive situation (7)
11 He being ill prepared to be a medieval Italian party man (10)
12 A thousand and one women organised to give you the bird (4)
14 The drink that goes to one's head (8)
16 Metal leg broken to give you a thrill (6)
17 Strike on the governor's day off (3)
19 Irritates not to have the right joints (6)
21 Perfume finally identified in seaweed (8)
24 Some much-loved enchanted garden (4)
25 Providers of incense, by gum! (4-6)
27 Feed from a lake (7)
28 Delicate paper in the dossier (7)
29 Where there's an arm ready for a sly production (2,4,6)

DOWN

1 Starting to be sick and ill when leaving port (7)
2 Appeals for directions to achieve agreements (10)
3 Odd exercises show copper to be untruthful (8)
4 Seeing it isn't in the centre of light (6)
5 Left to get a drink (4)
6 Eyeing the shelter when on call (7)
7 Dance when in a state to get wound up (8,4)
10 Does one put on worthless clothes to prepare stomach food? (5-7)
13 A nice title may show one's qualified (10)
15 Round up someone you know (3)
18 Opera to strike up if taken in by a small girl (8)
20 Ella joins Pat at a joint (7)
22 Refuse to go down lower (7)
23 Get wind of someone being tedious over Anglo-Saxon (6)
26 Bare one's teeth at endless hard work (4)

38

ACROSS

6 It's normal to establish who you are (5,9)

9 Has difficulty knowing when one's disturbed (6)

10 Man with a passion to shelter a service person (8)

11 They may want to buy a silk top and jumpers (8)

13 At home with a domestic group the Italian has left a bad reputation (6)

15 Disapprove of getting led astray by money (6)

17 Hold up and tie in a knot (6)

19 Old money may be seen as a gift (6)

20 Car Nadia crashed living the simple life (8)

22 Talk of the opposition (8)

24 Hat girl in a novel setting (6)

26 Player on the outside (6,8)

DOWN

1 Stand drinks at a launching (4,3,4,3)

2 Refuse to provide a vessel (4)

3 Look good when a knight loses a great deal (6)

4 Cite Ivan as being quite idle (8)

5 Commotion possibly caused by spooning (4)

7 Lay out money when you've lost your shirt? (6)

8 One may be expected to adopt a martial air (10,4)

12 Examine a very cheap dress (5)

14 Get priest to check it out if there's trickery (5)

16 Able to read it in the French class (8)

18 Opening a university requires some delicacy (6)

21 Related to an animal found hanging on a tree (6)

23 Compete with the West in showing vision (4)

25 Paddy and others endlessly showing the flag (4)

39

ACROSS

1 Pies cooked in anticipation of making way for water (8)
5 One has to make cuts at the highest level (6)
9 Test of ability in part (8)
10 Overhead canal? (6)
12 Be grateful there's no heat for a war machine (4)
13 Contrives to present a feature among friends (10)
15 Keenness of foreigners to show some taste (6,7)
19 One has tickets for those who shouldn't be there (7,6)
23 Choice of quiet location on the map (10)
25 Give voice to a lot of rot (4)
28 Not having sunk to being one to take milk round (6)
29 Dodgy dealer getting the message (8)
30 Being who you are without instincts (6)
31 Afraid to be given guidance after beginning (8)

DOWN

1 Enthusiastic shout about pictures (6)
2 Bother us and there'll be trouble here (5)
3 Regret to find devoutness lacks heart (4)
4 Dry air so out of place among the politically correct (7)
6 Not the first time there's been an increase in weight (5)
7 One may be on line to join a flotation (4-5)
8 Dad and Rosie found out where to watch the cars go by (8)
11 Not quite a fool, friend! (4)
14 Gathering for work with loud complaint (4)
15 Girl concealing her years allowed something to play (9)
16 The way to demonstrate there's no bending (3)
17 Splash in the drink (4)
18 Don't let an attendant go on strike (8)
20 What talkers do to the fat (4)
21 Old battered can that is not without its ring (7)
22 To brief the bishop I would become emotional (6)
24 Demand only what's just right (5)
26 Not getting a rise either way (5)
27 Asking a lot of the beloved (4)

40

ACROSS

1 Failing to achieve a brief appearance (11)
9 Getting a friend to take six back inside is of crucial importance (7)
10 Footwork has a revolutionary effect on it (7)
11 Sound depressed as one of the herd (3)
12 Give a girl a shout outside the food factory (7)
13 Repeat amendments to endless treaties (7)
14 Look as if you understand (3)
15 As fast as you can go when the road has all-round illumination (5)
17 Good and big (5)
18 Fish points not easily understood (5)
20 Having a cargo left at a port (5)
22 Take too much nonsense that won't wash (3)
24 Any temp can work out what's needed to secure purchase (7)
25 Something old set against that which is French (7)
26 Something poisonous like a non-sickness pill (3)
27 Leaderless rebellion brought to book (7)
28 Wrongly takes a sporting judge to be in error retreating (7)
29 Sally is one's ruin when not much is happening (5,6)

DOWN

1 Devils Andy's seen producing bad behaviour (5,6,4)
2 Porridge maker getting zero rating at providing something to eat (7)
3 Not much time for a friend to make a reckoning (5)
4 Scorned to go beyond the centre ground to be cheated (9)
5 Such coldness is mostly below the surface (7)
6 Divine appeal by singers of standing (3,4,3,5)
7 There's nothing in them (6)
8 When you have to cede a new position it shows cunning (6)
16 Aggressive behaviour transgressing the limit making a girl lose her head (9)
18 Metal may take an arresting form (6)
19 Particular example of men getting away with nearly everything (7)
21 Causes pain and annoyance (7)
23 Slippery when in the shade (6)
25 Fruit pip without one in the drink (5)

41

ACROSS

1 Showed the way to the sharp end (7)
5 The beauty of a very cheap ring (6)
9 Some err badly and show penitence (7)
10 Gypsy concealing high mind at work (7)
11 Angry setback for mother (3)
12 Ten more star turns protest (11)
13 Backward pupil making slow speech (5)
14 Need rally to be organised in scholarly style (9)
16 Cutting one out of the sequence set in a river (9)
17 Keep going this way to get back where you started (5)
19 Preparing to take things with you when you travel in a crate (7-4)
22 Ready for the whole lot! (3)
23 The record is something poetic as it happens (7)
24 Start praying about quarrel at the top of the church (7)
26 We're all at one in this (6)
27 Business with a couple of pounds takes in one army man (7)

DOWN

1 Girl in the swim standing up to display a solid figure (7)
2 Getting something done now, one takes it (9,6)
3 Rubbish piled up to a height (3)
4 Fancy it might be the last hundred sheets of paper (5)
5 One has to be there at a time when the poet hasn't finished (9)
6 Gasp about one display of colour (5)
7 Do you think this clumsy or just embarrassing? (7,8)
8 Cook fish inside without prompting (6)
12 Something surviving from a scene of dereliction (5)
14 Feel anger and turn colour (4-5)
15 Tend to read the runes inaccurately (5)
16 Advise backing the favourite and one may be carried shoulder-high (6)
18 Devoted to rising trade union in possibly fluid circumstances (7)
20 Presses on in couples when the old man's not there (5)
21 Like a small representation of a jelly (5)
25 Nothing but the end missing from the line-up (3)

42

ACROSS

1 Fencing damaged when given a push (3,3,6)
8 Time to be right behind business backing (7)
9 Coming up with a rebellion (7)
11 Hate to cheer baron doing wrong (10)
12 Very sensible in a way (4)
14 Unhealthy seed said to have been scattered (8)
16 Judges sound methods (6)
17 Hurry for a drink and a bite (3)
19 Put pennies in the hat to get drink (6)
21 Sank a pit into the land (8)
24 Instrument of honour – there's nothing in it! (4)
25 Winner to object early in the morning (5,5)
27 Catching up on profit (7)
28 Prosper from debt the gang went round and brought back (7)
29 Where strikes aren't allowed under hold-up circumstances (5,3,4)

DOWN

1 Gets hold of a rotten cheat in the Civil Service (7)
2 Place of worship that can later be rebuilt (10)
3 Alternative Poles not quite correct for Vikings (8)
4 Canter around in a daze (6)
5 Fall in behind the gunners (4)
6 Climbing up half-heartedly with light effect (7)
7 Fired with the power to be very fierce (3,3,6)
10 Supposing it's fun when you don't know the answers (8,4)
13 Purple line written by last British-American poet (10)
15 Go in for what might be lucky (3)
18 Good enough to get by (8)
20 Expert on the line to give you the picture (7)
22 Woolly pair that sent wit crazy (4-3)
23 Gifted with the ability to keep moving (6)
26 Nothing to put up and nothing on the floor (4)

43

ACROSS

6 Uses Anne's plant to cause trouble (14)
9 Keeps in big shops (6)
10 Removal of former prisoner – one is back inside (8)
11 One old side that may be much admired (8)
13 Kind people contributing to a build-up (6)
15 Close to perfection (6)
17 Fancy free perhaps in seeking publicity (6)
19 Good cover for inferior (6)
20 Tell a lunkhead not to be stuffy (8)
22 Censure one for turning back into a fool (8)
24 Suppose there could be money in a sea excursion (6)
26 What tells actors the way to the theatre? (5,9)

DOWN

1 Leave journalist if travelling free with conservationists to see transformation made (5,9)
2 Incentive to accomplish some of one's purposes (4)
3 One comes to them when consciousness returns (6)
4 Where you might take a bite from a bran cask (5-3)
5 One has to leave the opposition workers (4)
7 Faithful to the firm (6)
8 Electrifying attack on wrong thinking (5,9)
12 The man has a point (5)
14 Work out how to make a finer adjustment (5)
16 Not worried about sales device for a song (8)
18 King about to be accepted at length (6)
21 Land far out at the end of resistance (6)
23 Wild indulgence of otherwise heartless fellow (4)
25 Some cards that might be appropriate (4)

44

ACROSS

1 Tree starting to crack when on fire perhaps (7)
5 Take cattle to sound like leaves in the wind (6)
9 Have a word when letters are sorted again (7)
10 Big distance for an artist to travel – what nonsense! (7)
11 Waves from some of those already arrived (3)
12 Not in favour of adapting the point of gadget (11)
13 Is an Old Etonian able to keep one afloat? (5)
14 Looking back the animal presents an awful appearance (9)
16 Regret having to write one number when given little choice at last (9)
17 Burst out with pure reactionary twaddle at first (5)
19 Take only what's suitable (11)
22 Very angry when there's not a thing to look at (3)
23 Given sweet treatment when the container was late (7)
24 Put on pale dip preparation (7)
26 There's a lot of money to be made from breaking the law (6)
27 Money paid out for enclosures in the river (7)

DOWN

1 Finest people learning to be in charge (7)
2 Well turned out compared with how little money one has (4,2,9)
3 A long way to go with service coming up (3)
4 Holy Empire person (5)
5 Mention of a testimonial (9)
6 Fight for very little (5)
7 Most important issue with a suggested answer (7,8)
8 German capital and French cover (6)
12 Box giving a person a front view (5)
14 The one that always makes a century (9)
15 Row made during a play (5)
16 Bound to see Mandela's supporters before going round (6)
18 One has to get going when you put your foot down (7)
20 College of advanced views (5)
21 Conscious of what the movement has left behind (5)
25 One of those that tell the time causing annoyance (3)

45

ACROSS

1 Talk of fighting the last of the issue in underground passages (6-6)
8 Without thinking of being rude (7)
9 Licking the baby's head in an expression of sorrow (7)
11 A toil in sun maybe helping to keep warm (10)
12 It may move one to reach the heights (4)
14 Greatness not entirely out of line for a soldier (8)
16 Economical cover in a Cornish river (6)
17 Figure worshipped in a Chinese pagoda (3)
19 Powerful fellow-man (6)
21 Wrong thing to take away when it's time for enjoyment (5,3)
24 Thought I would go to East Africa briefly (4)
25 One's in the same state as oneself (10)
27 What's doing if you refuse? (7)
28 Spinners require lubrication on the surface (3-4)
29 Rustled up RAs to organise more selling than buying (5,7)

DOWN

1 Person employing an arbitrator one doesn't accept (7)
2 Certainly agreed, anyway (2,3,5)
3 Composing at home can be included in research (8)
4 Statement of wishes made with painful cry and possibly weeping (6)
5 Inclination to become a swindle (4)
6 Gaining equally before the night's out (7)
7 Result of plane going through bad weather warning? (5,7)
10 Empty talk of keeping dry in a hat when something shabby is let out (6-6)
13 Curve they turned over to a friend on the original model (10)
15 Weight of stuffing taken from the station (3)
18 Turn up in direst distress to find one arguing (8)
20 Like London in its Council days (7)
22 Honour one has the sense to find threatening (7)
23 Tricks to avoid contact (6)
26 Gain only fourth grade – that's a blow! (4)

46

ACROSS

6 Result of sickness benefit fraud? (3-6,5)

9 Complain about hewing being done badly (6)

10 One sent by ecstasy will fail to get a fine (8)

11 Pretended to be deeply moved (8)

13 One's responsible for what appears between the covers (6)

15 Teased for being badly dressed (6)

17 Information provided by a girl in the lake (6)

19 Lady not against revealing the position (6)

20 Characteristic of real estate (8)

22 Back a girl on to a tree that's fallen from one side to the other (8)

24 Tone down the passion (6)

26 Anxious to stress that jittery feeling (7,7)

DOWN

1 Only one guess needed (5,5,4)

2 Go off the bottle when something to eat is offered (4)

3 Harry, the spy at the heart of the question (6)

4 Be a good friend and drop a hint (8)

5 High standing of the girl you first abandoned (4)

7 We have to appear in a man's clothes (6)

8 Christmas accommodation problem (2,4,2,3,3)

12 Nigel performs a reel in Scotland (5)

14 Wanting to soothe? You can say that again! (5)

16 Lively girl having wild fun with the little lieutenant (8)

18 Ghost with guts (6)

21 Public exposure during an excursion (6)

23 Go ahead and arouse feeling (4)

25 Most important person to have around one (4)

47

ACROSS

1 The state of the beetle (8)
5 Way of getting at American eminence (6)
9 One's left out of regulation military supplies (8)
10 Silent about work for the repository (6)
12 Cut the number of sailors employed (4)
13 Turn out in place of what's prosaic (10)
15 Not standing for being sensible? (5,8)
19 Like an angry sheep? (4,3,6)
23 Suitable gift for a cigarette-smoking man of property? (10)
25 Affected to provide temporary accommodation (4)
28 Animals kept dry in folded lace (6)
29 Talk expected to include one with a record (8)
30 Make more obscure study about a vessel (6)
31 One of the gang not having much on top (8)

DOWN

1 Bend down to see the King in bed (6)
2 Left in dodgy deal – scoop! (5)
3 Take in some of the more appealing young women (4)
4 Goodness, it's the last month to begin the Pope's letter! (7)
6 Faith in an arrangement for market control (5)
7 There's pain in Terry's awful betrayal (9)
8 Make a pretence of composing endless music before one's dead (8)
11 Fish with a musical finish (4)
14 Strip city (4)
15 One of those that get together for prayer or afterwards (9)
16 Service seat (3)
17 Strips the top off to get at the fish (4)
18 Deceitful couple having to be confronted (3-5)
20 Bob's unemployment benefit (4)
21 It's an honour to be weaving silk using Cleopatra's needle (7)
22 Hang on for a very quiet conclusion (6)
24 Be compelled to include what's left when you make a big reduction (5)
26 Make a case for a rascal leaving nothing out (5)
27 Dash out of the Channel Tunnel and escape the fire (4)

48

ACROSS

1 One sees a lot of drama in her great toe waggling (7-4)
9 One may cut what the journalist witnesses (7)
10 Record the destruction of green centrepiece (7)
11 Go down and lose royalty for a faulty performance (3)
12 Take over to lessen the pain (7)
13 One following a vehicle may show what's coming (7)
14 Transport firm losing one head (3)
15 She's got home to Australia first (5)
17 Hang about and get defiled (5)
18 They record what may be needed for a tie-up (5)
20 Fish the other end where there's light around (5)
22 Do the human thing (3)
24 Undertake to get something written about military intelligence (7)
25 Signifies Ted's one fault (7)
26 Some patriotic city (3)
27 Having enough money for an opening to the sun (7)
28 Celebrity embarrassed at being marked out (7)
29 Not the original costume for classic drama (6,5)

DOWN

1 Question of how to apply a sensitive touch (8,7)
2 Set near destabilisation of Asia (7)
3 Sweat out a means of punishment (5)
4 Turn out to be what happened when you last had a meal (9)
5 Do too much in the way of ham (7)
6 Professional soldier's face in the papers often (7,8)
7 Youngster hugging the girl who's angelic (6)
8 Almost at a point before time (6)
16 Burst ever a possibility when one's against government (9)
18 One's able to make clear what's written (6)
19 Pay for advice in dispatch (7)
21 Authority for a person to appear on a particular day (7)
23 Live to be a partisan again (6)
25 Given treatment at a party – but in Latin (5)

49

ACROSS

1 Bad rule made to last (7)
5 One looks after a flock that is gone or will follow (6)
9 Great person at the top showing conceit (3-4)
10 One has to decide what part to take in a rare disaster (7)
11 Ready for the whole lot (3)
12 Our Rosie and Tim having a virtuous involvement (11)
13 Mark will give support without us (5)
14 Display of temper when the sparks fly (9)
16 Sly employee having gone below (9)
17 Turncoat with a deficiency bringing in a team that can kill (5)
19 Picturing primitive transport as a guide to how the land lies? (11)
22 Regret a way the French have (3)
23 Showing where to get a drink when one's hung over maybe (3,4)
24 Bag girl in pursuit of publicity (7)
26 What really matters is not to get caught if one's a member of an ancient sect (6)
27 Chance to make a fortune but a man loses heart (7)

DOWN

1 Disturbing seabeds causes corruption (7)
2 Both sides of moral dilemmas (6,3,6)
3 Working gathering that makes one busy (3)
4 Describing home-made wine perhaps as having greater maturity (5)
5 Smeared as having had too much to drink – (9)
6 – not being in this condition (5)
7 It gets you moving away from home (7,8)
8 Little credit is given to a goddess in an emergency (6)
12 Youngster having no right to be on the motorway (5)
14 Sweet smell of paper in the country (9)
15 Amusing to find it in the middle of what you started (5)
16 Finish your feature, boy! (6)
18 Small measure of wine in good time as you see (7)
20 Compound to make an animal due perhaps (5)
21 It enables one to see who's learning (5)
25 Catch what's left after deductions (3)

50

ACROSS

1 Things to buy when you've an inclination to spend Sunday working in Kent (8,4)

8 Little girl in favour? (7)

9 Rotter keeping quiet about one metal (7)

11 Drew in five different ways to enable one to get the picture (10)

12 Current units used as a member goes in (4)

14 Ignore a concession (8)

16 Very hot in a habit or riding breeches (6)

17 Something sparkling brings the mystic back (3)

19 Look good with a man (6)

21 Bit of sound reception (8)

24 Takes in the last of military failure (4)

25 One classes the tiger upset about nothing as being among the players (10)

27 Assistance for a mug, would you say? (7)

28 One puts half a dozen on the list backing one to reach the heights (7)

29 Two places provided irregularly in the area (4,3,5)

DOWN

1 Tries out new way in craft for feminists (7)

2 Having no contact with skill (3,2,5)

3 It's publicity time and Vera starts to leave making herself look good (8)

4 Metal not worth much in America (6)

5 Good to get out of the house to find a lot of metal (4)

6 Having a stroke keeps one going (7)

7 Serious Australians providing openings at last (12)

10 Met under visa difficulties by accident (12)

13 Arrive almost at an assurance of accommodation (10)

15 Support needed when driving off (3)

18 Get tied up when you increase speed (4,4)

20 Clear it to be edited as a newspaper item (7)

22 Pet lies supplied in written form (7)

23 No children about in the store (6)

26 Cut up by leading European national (4)

ACROSS

6 Love matters in government (7,2,5)
9 Loved to make a fuss when embarrassed (6)
10 Tale of the whole Orient being soaked in blood (8)
11 Hard cone moved to be made secure (8)
13 Quietly go higher than usual (6)
15 Run and get a big drink (6)
17 Give agreement when made to go (6)
19 Told to make an offer to study (6)
20 Made a comeback as new Red revolutionary (8)
22 Design home label for the return of fuel (8)
24 Tempt learner to take four letters away (6)
26 Angry allusion to the need to look elsewhere (5-9)

DOWN

1 One's had a tough time being bad (8,6)
2 A long way from owning a farm in Provence (4)
3 Arrest at the end of a march in Socialist rising (6)
4 A first floor apartment of American inspiration (8)
5 No woman could be such a beast! (4)
7 Drink and be cautious all round (6)
8 Way of getting more tight according to James? (4,2,3,5)
12 Harry the dog (5)
14 Not all one may have to say (5)
16 Come down and see the way one runs a pub (8)
18 Outcome of a job loss (3-3)
21 Gives directions on a ranch maybe (6)
23 It may be as well to take some meals out (4)
25 Accent on colour (4)

52

ACROSS

1 Big deficit in what's been dug out (8)
5 Not quite right when learning to drive (6)
9 Aura of quiet madness attached to the son I have (8)
10 Success for the cause (6)
12 They may be put in to advance the craft (4)
13 Prejudiced later in not being able to adapt (10)
15 Over there where a pelican might get you (6,3,4)
19 Unfriendly faces assembled by a crooked art dealer? (6,7)
23 Graduate to lechery with dear dancer on the terrace maybe (10)
25 The going-over of a lifetime (4)
28 A cup for the old folk (6)
29 Dressing to cover what might be shot tissue (8)
30 Bingo's legs (6)
31 Suffering from nothing but bad behaviour back among the old (8)

DOWN

1 Often seen as vulgar (6)
2 Light concentration in hospital – a serious matter (5)
3 Uncover a way to descend mountains to the north (4)
4 Old boy supplying medical item to students (7)
6 Not much without the top gun (5)
7 Hunting for politician before American prosecutor goes ahead (9)
8 Freedom to make lines on a map (8)
11 Warning? That's a laugh! (4)
14 Interpret as banishing criminals to be seen as honest (4)
15 High-flier taking the prize for divine food (5-4)
16 Sunny country – not in spring (3)
17 Need harrow for the garden (4)
18 Likely to favour confusion in Babel (8)
20 Boast a get-up one can wear (4)
21 Finding a home for a stray dog found in the heather (7)
22 Got together as a team maybe (6)
24 Investment in the Heron company (5)
26 Iron demand (5)
27 Sailor's rise with the fleet in store (4)

1 2 3 4 5 6 7 8
9 10
11
12 13
14
15 16 17
18
19 20 21
22
23 24 25 26
27
28 29
30 31

53

ACROSS

1 Well-fed vegetarian in high spirits (4,2,5)
9 Wonder if you see an empty creel in the mud (7)
10 One doesn't read everything as master of a craft (7)
11 Like Harry to start making a deposit (3)
12 Having taken turns to get more tick (7)
13 Go too far in connection with retreat (7)
14 Some measure of embellishment (3)
15 Become a competitor to make a record (5)
17 Big input into the ones over there (5)
18 Couples said to provide fruit (5)
20 Award mark for having got round (5)
22 Drop off down (3)
24 Finish without so much going on (7)
25 Be angry about hothead's light dance (7)
26 The way teetotaller starts to become a drinker (3)
27 What's concluded in that place where there's war (7)
28 Those having boisterous fun might suit baby (7)
29 Get ready to fly like an angel (6,5)

DOWN

1 Talk of a take-off (8,7)
2 Scold for badly cut reel (7)
3 Nymph with nothing to study (5)
4 See office (9)
5 Food for people in a tail-spin (7)
6 Better songs for the majority (8,7)
7 Come out east to get myself and Reg moving (6)
8 Eminent person of CPRE (6)
16 Union outfit finally left by a philosopher (9)
18 Rather well placed for sitting (6)
19 Cover for hard employer (7)
21 His job is on the line (7)
23 Father turns up in a pub to die (6)
25 Labour's Jack the Hat (5)

54

ACROSS

1 Linen for the crib Mac brought round (7)
5 The endless scramble to see a singer (6)
9 Check the day the riot got out of control (7)
10 Sweet fool coming back before the fall (7)
11 Growth from something Hazel must have planted (3)
12 Approve a collection of features (11)
13 Feeling the strain when a number seem to lose the measure (5)
14 Catering expert with the ability to look ahead (9)
16 Willing to put transport back on board (9)
17 One doesn't start a fire here (5)
19 Men do tune in to what may be kept secret (11)
22 Force cancellation of cutback that leaves one cold (3)
23 Man's in a mess, the dope (7)
24 Dirty accommodation covered by high water (3-4)
26 Bind the listener at last (6)
27 This rep could be one of the beat generation (7)

DOWN

1 Remark on what the French say (7)
2 Big society person with grave responsibilities (10,5)
3 Depression at the heart of reality (3)
4 Island in the Adriatic or further south (5)
5 Little scope for a walker to avoid dangerous alternatives (5-4)
6 Love to leave one church for another (5)
7 One's modest about making little bloomer (9,6)
8 Organ of malice (6)
12 A number remaining when there's been a split (5)
14 Somewhere to drink with Shirley not finally involved as a book person (9)
15 Epic Irish legislators getting one up (5)
16 Sensitive turn-out – Cherry can't go wrong! (6)
18 Supporter who makes one cross (7)
20 Sound one in front (5)
21 Girl from American city on speed (5)
25 Put in for a qualification shortly (3)

55

ACROSS

1 One goes up and down childishly without getting anywhere (7-5)
8 Fairly slow with the advance payment (7)
9 Starts to get round outfit in the south (7)
11 Distinctive feature of Italy? Spice in cooking (10)
12 He makes a true move leaving an address (4)
14 Rubber woman (8)
16 I'm first, you're second (6)
17 Fiery saint lacking nothing but wood (3)
19 Little one able to move fast (6)
21 Class fee modified if no features are offered (8)
24 Get rid of some of the most notorious terrorists (4)
25 Course to take in our possibly no-good poet (10)
27 One has to learn to deal with stunted characters (7)
28 When there's a drift back one has to get on producing a book (7)
29 Dotty way of figuring things out (6,6)

DOWN

1 Put right after take-off? (7)
2 Unable to get to one bar when there's a projection (10)
3 Think perfect thought and get awful lies (8)
4 Got concerned about decay in cave (6)
5 Don't show the way to get into religious writing (4)
6 Suppresses the less fit perhaps (7)
7 Mean to knock up the man who has debts (12)
10 Support another line (6,6)
13 Striking hand shields injured leader who supports union (10)
15 Little chap won't keep quiet on the level (3)
18 Covering university bank in adult fashion (8)
20 Carriage of letters over a river (7)
22 Self-esteem for instance turning moist (7)
23 Credit is given it by one cold analyst (6)
26 River erosion (4)

56

ACROSS

6 Up from all fours so to speak? (2,4,4,4)

9 Grass as one of a class (6)

10 Among devious moles a person lacks company (8)

11 It may be made the answer (8)

13 No end of surprise on seeing the river (6)

15 Get into trouble producing part of a meal when it's wanted (2,4)

17 Support for a short time (6)

19 Perfect example of how meaning may be expressed (6)

20 Girl allowed back to deliver a message (8)

22 It might give the cellar a going-over (8)

24 To keep needling for a long time is such waste! (6)

26 Cheerful after a drink or two to activate the brain? (5,3,6)

DOWN

1 Where one might go to find bygones (4,6,4)

2 Game cut up all round (4)

3 They're partial to not very clever ministerial pests (6)

4 Swamp Nina with duet badly arranged (8)

5 A final endless expression or regret (4)

7 It could bring a horse to a standstill (6)

8 Fun you can have blowing through openings? (4,2,8)

12 Area outside the house in occupation (5)

14 The way to go to make progress (5)

16 Crazy girl besotted with a song (8)

18 Made a show of making way for old people (6)

21 There's something licentious about glory (6)

23 Instrument not giving true sound (4)

25 Pay for beginning to waste time (4)

57

ACROSS

1 Mo appears to be in heaven some nights (4-4)
5 Investigates quiet cover-ups (6)
9 One might cut exercises when North Korea needs fine adjustment (8)
10 Drink all round with the French on the roof maybe (6)
12 Animals put to work, you might say (4)
13 Clarification of what constitutes good manners (10)
15 Bad language disguised yet put out between harmless shots (8,5)
19 Making patterns on a cold surface (6-7)
23 Number causing tension for a woman entertainer (10)
25 Strike friends for going the wrong way (4)
28 Not the street for a meeting (3-3)
29 Dead and gone (8)
30 One might have a trying time over a bed (6)
31 Reduce requirements when there's no demand (8)

DOWN

1 Connection required for a double-barrelled name (6)
2 Dive without starting to charge (5)
3 Money-making plant (4)
4 Away to the mountain when not too busy (3-4)
6 Usual procedure not getting in the way (5)
7 One's able to make a comeback when thrown out (9)
8 Cross and ruined as Kit was (8)
11 Heard the shot was unsuccessful in poor visibility (4)
14 Retreat from learning music (4)
15 Lacking finish they have much to learn (9)
16 What a beast the Spanish monarch could be! (3)
17 Edge of sulphur stone (4)
18 Branch out and try to make a killing (8)
20 Brisk look round the river (4)
21 Forbidding to use rate differential (7)
22 Suit those that get stuck in the ground (6)
24 Invitation to be friends that may lack firmness (5)
26 To get a bit playful it requires some drink (5)
27 A magician may have it in hand (4)

ACROSS

1 Be fully aware of the Zero girl (4,7)
9 Give out all round (7)
10 Everyone on top when it's finished (3,4)
11 Able to be repeated in a dance (3)
12 Make contact with officer – idle to dissemble! (7)
13 Silence if a man is moved (7)
14 Place that's very disturbing to us (3)
15 Saw nothing being drunk in low surroundings (5)
17 Be prone to get cut short by the master (5)
18 Tears around fixing pay scales (5)
20 Runs into gatherings for pursuits (5)
22 Time to mature (3)
24 Improve appearance with a high hemline? (5,2)
25 Little chaps not letting beards grow (7)
26 Little Alan leaves a girl cold (3)
27 Singers' task embracing nearly everything (7)
28 Complain at a method of getting people moving (7)
29 Offer it might be safer to refuse (6,5)

DOWN

1 Not going to extremes of dangerous driving? (6,2,3,4)
2 Suit mad kink for watching sports (7)
3 Your daughter may be mine, brother (5)
4 Switch posts near reorganisation (9)
5 How badly Shakespeare expresses spite (3-4)
6 Make a present of pheasants to show what you've been up to? (4,3,4,4)
7 Said to be one of the bigger shopkeepers (6)
8 Start life here with dodgy deal on credit (6)
16 See how long it takes to get a man on board to give you tick (9)
18 Make cuts that could have cured the beginning of embonpoint (6)
19 Mark has to hold our people to keep up (7)
21 Standing at one's post (7)
23 Tries Elia's output (6)
25 Finish these to drink some blood (5)

59

ACROSS

1 Funny business with spurious claim (7)
5 Resolve to throw some police into the river (6)
9 Morning before the day one has a gas (7)
10 Top expert on the crest of a wave (7)
11 It's set to bring a time of darkness (3)
12 Tried new way of thinking that could be harmful (11)
13 Game for a good loser (5)
14 Somewhere to live away from others (9)
16 Cement mortar no doubt producing coolness (9)
17 One might enclose money (5)
19 At home a stupid one gradually loses fat in easy-going fashion (11)
22 Make a hit dancing (3)
23 Wash to see if eels can wriggle (7)
24 Carry on for certain about five to four (7)
26 Appearance of a watcher without returning the register (6)
27 A sitter disturbed by a performer (7)

DOWN

1 Frame the little prince with his sibling (7)
2 Little time to lose marbles (6,2,7)
3 Study to deceive (3)
4 Grass on a good person – that's as low as one can get! (5)
5 Is a little drink during the day going to waste? (9)
6 Have a bad word for the dog at a loose end (5)
7 How to prevent outsiders gaining insight (4,3,8)
8 Hide some of what's left inside and have a ball (6)
12 Same again – little Dorothy's crazy about it? (5)
14 Inspiring figure meant to wander around having fun (9)
15 Growing girl spinner, it's easy to conclude (5)
16 Definitely settle for an embrace (6)
18 Allow to fall into deep broken drain (7)
20 The point of a cavalry attack (5)
21 Act so unsuitable for opera (5)
25 One betrays a little beastliness (3)

60

ACROSS

1 Problem with animal in a tree (6-6)
8 Chap getting cross applying punishment to a creature without end (4,3)
9 Imitative story starting to get exaggerated (7)
11 Creature with no rich resources offering love (10)
12 Sound content to turn up with a posh car (4)
14 They're crazy to cut nails out (8)
16 Band heard to come to a standstill (6)
17 Performer in a meaty part (3)
19 Bundle criminal out of world-wide trade without raising a smile (6)
21 One's made dispositions for departure (8)
24 Encourages to provide food (4)
25 Made to appear dense if idolised unsuitably (10)
27 Not allowing Poles to get to Peterhead without delay (3-4)
28 Make dense countryman take a number round (7)
29 Train a companion for forming young acquaintance (6-6)

DOWN

1 No mains have been laid out to the big house (7)
2 Old devil appearing periodically at the critical moment (4,2,4)
3 Get dug in at the centre without heading for Norwich or Women's Institute outing (8)
4 One goes in and out to help get things moving (6)
5 Keenness in competing for a prize always helps (4)
6 Lie around if convinced there's time to spare (7)
7 Colour stone to attract the gullible (7,5)
10 Nag for a change of ownership in hard bargaining (5-7)
13 This could be the death of you, brother! (10)
15 The day you took the exam (3)
18 Press and TV take on eminence as go-between (8)
20 Natural circuit for racing round (7)
22 Deceived by Paddy the fatherless Edward suffers shortage (7)
23 You may have to move for a short period, it's true (6)
26 He's found the lowest central position (4)

CRYPTIC

6 A space to fold away, perhaps containing 30 (4)
7 A ... with a twist in story in the end. That's good! (6)
8 Take a tip ... (6,4) ... look back on a device ...
9 Sea bream ... to help up by ... (4)
9 The search of Columbus in plain view, we hear (6)
11 Raw ... was around the cupboard (5)
12 It's ... cause of a wild message end of month (4)
... could be 30 al ... (6) Doctor here (6)
16 We ... hope you'll see them? (4)
19 Poetical T V slot ... lunch ... for drugs power ... (6)
21 included point for purpose tag (4)
22 To catch ... E within the ... here to and outlast snooker? (4)
25 ... may have to cover his ... out period. It's told (6)
28 with a wild firework ... cases for (4,6)

61

ACROSS

6 Up to every sin in dubious place of learning (4,10)
9 An excessive desire is not disputed (6)
10 Policeman posing possible danger to myself (8)
11 Picture Rita getting fuddled after a drink (8)
13 Herbal remedy for the credulous (6)
15 State there's no barrier to eternal punishment (6)
17 Rage on about being an ass (6)
19 Splendid line in fancy dress (6)
20 It may produce a sticky situation grounding flight (4-4)
22 Too much to take (8)
24 Making better copper ornament (6)
26 Where surfing can be carried on successfully (5,2,3,4)

DOWN

1 A villain's underwear is bad for the liver (4,4,6)
2 Live with half-dead historian (4)
3 Crazy get-up for Doctor Arbuthnot first seen in the Arctic (6)
4 Catch up with New York boy poet (8)
5 To Euthan it could mean death out East (4)
7 Bars being admitted to move on the way up (6)
8 One might be given it when the clock strikes (6,8)
12 When there's a bird he is given only a small part (5)
14 Powerful personality given little time to pull up (5)
16 Ring a couple of unknowns and some idiot will provide a contradiction (8)
18 Don't agree to a thing! (6)
21 The sound of criminal activity (6)
23 Rub the other end and see a snake (4)
25 Wander around with a male taking nothing in (4)

62

ACROSS

1 Spoil the resting-place of a noble foreigner (8)
5 Showed great feeling when getting a book back to prepare for publication without it (6)
9 Half of North America is on the line to learn something here (8)
10 Where a going-over might get you (6)
12 Being thin one gets plastered (4)
13 Several get the big picture in bed (4-6)
15 Given indications of kisses when the romance goes wrong? (7,2,4)
19 In which steps may be taken to change partners (6-2,5)
23 Say if you can fit together (10)
25 Agreement obtained in a late Parliamentary session (4)
28 The right thing to provide a fix at the end of a stint (6)
29 No fair trial at such a beastly court (8)
30 Visionary girl following the Red revolution (6)
31 Become dull with no women to throw a net over (8)

DOWN

1 Go in with a show of strength (6)
2 Send the clock up (5)
3 Called to give a climber help (4)
4 Virginia finds somewhere in South America and North America to be different (7)
6 Protection needed on a circuit of overseas Portugal (5)
7 Attack repeated in a small engine (3-6)
8 One who's left for the wilderness? (8)
11 Trained to be a thorough racer (4)
14 Little ones going on foot (4)
15 Mark Channel Islands animal taking food (9)
16 See what emerges from the Year of the Millennium (3)
17 When finishing a person doesn't find any (4)
18 Dead and gone (8)
20 Pole leaving a man some way to go (4)
21 Take away from the land when trade has come to an end (7)
22 Resort to what's approved in a different vein (6)
24 Best get an egghead to teach intensively all round (5)
26 She does a first-rate push-up (5)
27 Eager to make a move and get started (4)

63

ACROSS

1 One of the pack acting as a character (7-4)
9 Go ahead softly before having to go back (7)
10 Awful rat bite on priest's head (7)
11 Nice comparison, sweetie! (3)
12 Understanding of what's not hidden (7)
13 Red Star transport enables them to do business (7)
14 Traitor taken aback by something sticky (3)
15 Don't start talking like Paddy, the scoundrel! (5)
17 String out last drink (5)
18 Gas used in a move to get among the warships (5)
20 Had to make a confession (5)
22 There's something in Thatcherism that goes to one's head (3)
24 Sneaking fellow of dubious virtue (7)
25 Teacher turns on boy offering food (7)
26 Try to get justice for the girl (3)
27 One's foolish to protect the lady when there's smoke (7)
28 Getting used to possible ruin by swilling gin (7)
29 Protection for a traveller's lying (8-3)

DOWN

1 Plots to provide enjoyment (8,7)
2 One makes some return for wrongdoing (7)
3 Clumsy write-up in information technology (5)
4 Move to keep opponents apart as a mediator (2-7)
5 A rotter having the right to be seen as on the level (7)
6 Act in a properly Conservative way (2,3,5,5)
7 Be quick to publish when the crisis is finally over (6)
8 Gets only partial rest when there's trouble (6)
16 Foolish carry-on in military style (5-4)
18 Pretend to have influence (6)
19 Refuse to give one a quantity that's harmful (7)
21 Birds' trade union quickly formed to cause trouble (7)
23 Somewhere depressing to get beastly food (6)
25 Be on top in the fall, say (5)

64

ACROSS

1 Letters received after a shooting (4-3)
5 Choose a group to capture the French (6)
9 List duck held to be a different bird (7)
10 Hit the drink to get sympathy (7)
11 Part at the end of a lot of talk (3)
12 Seems in bate when troubled by frequent times away (11)
13 Take a turn in Clare's place – endless tedium (5)
14 Grub her ma might produce when food is wanted (9)
16 When nearly everything is said to have disappeared one of the five has to be brave (9)
17 Overweight without any take-aways (5)
19 Not moved to become mutinous (11)
22 Get more without one going back to complain (3)
23 Credit American agitation for providing old European money (7)
24 Free to see about occupation for a time (7)
26 Take the top job and make a killing (6)
27 Ask for directions to the celebrations (7)

DOWN

1 Knock up clever story (7)
2 Generous sign of having played the game (8,7)
3 One of those mad characters among the bells (3)
4 Makes bloody use of tapering material (5)
5 Powerful figure of holy person and upright type no good inside (9)
6 Goes all round the cathedral centre in error (5)
7 Finally drinks beer where bargains may be had (7-4,4)
8 Must be wrong if royalty shows it's a dud (6)
12 Get into a row (5)
14 Bingo's call to get a grip in a domestic situation (9)
15 Pressed for some home-made grub to be served up (5)
16 Tot one takes to court when one's hooked (6)
18 Encourage our people to stand on the street and make proposals (7)
20 Set up to give protection all round (5)
21 However many there might be (5)
25 Fifty to put up is quite a number (3)

Crossword grid numbered: 1, 2, 3, 4, 5, 6, 7, 8, 9, 10, 11, 12, 13, 14, 15, 16, 17, 18, 19, 20, 21, 22, 23, 24, 25, 26, 27

4 That of the state is always of use (and SO).
7 Inside the concluding thought... (6)
8 Ploy that seek to its vice ... won long than the
   attempt
9 Up of a certain day (include stems mast) or (7)
7 Pronounced (8) we that light could be finest of
10 Over the county they's ... handball you might is (9)
   (15 Spoken ... me (9)
14 Coming ... of Olympia kept for simple tot ... soph (10)
15 Spoon that she to no other part to be attended (9)
16 To forgiveness ... one batter ... being against ... (4)
23 Blushing may ... complete ... of the ... feet ... (12)
    Philosophy is present (8) ... time is over ... (9)
20 Opath ... matter ... of exploration (5) ... d
21 Programs ... may ... thiele ... (4-2)
22 The ... in part from a man ... (4)

65

ACROSS

1 Battling magistrate maybe getting things wrong (5,7)
8 Charges little one to stir the suet (7)
9 Concerned with getting proper echo (7)
11 Dance with Jack before everybody comes back (10)
12 She's as honoured as you are, Sir (4)
14 Gave up work without resisting (8)
16 The trick is to sound as if breathing's difficult (6)
17 Research wisecrack (3)
19 Endless cannabis taken by one youngster could be a killer (6)
21 Could be carried by no ordinary seaman at the end of a voyage (8)
24 Father's left word you've got the part (4)
25 Having groups of sheriff's men to provide entertainment (10)
27 Man's lie capable of development (7)
28 After a month in France some get wet (7)
29 One's able to find the words that give you the picture (6-6)

DOWN

1 Tells of hearing guns go off (7)
2 Out of bed with evil intent? (2,2,2,4)
3 Wasn't slow to get out when the Danes appeared (8)
4 Run wild, take the first of the month off and become rowdy (6)
5 Something to do with the day you turned up to start knitting (4)
6 Bottle anger after business takes a turn (7)
7 If you can't have a hot time these could be fun (6,6)
10 See Enid in leg show – that might get things going! (6,6)
13 Spotless undercoat (5,5)
15 Go down briefly to keep the little girl quiet (3)
18 Try different smears to achieve very fine stuff (8)
20 Religious eleven about to strike before getting caught (7)
22 Swelling like a second-rate cataloguer (7)
23 Material could explode if nothing is taken up (6)
26 One of those that give support for prayer (4)

66

ACROSS

6 Force to leave the ship when Chuck is company chairman (5,9)

9 Broken plates of a delicate colour (6)

10 Fish seen in a painful light (5-3)

11 Impressed by the elephant heading the charge (8)

13 Smart turn in dubious taste (6)

15 Protest at umpire's disallowing an appeal? (6)

17 Forgotten relic of an earlier time (6)

19 Coming to see an opening for sales boost (6)

20 Sort of expense incurred in wearing a hat (8)

22 Drove round with a person being carried too far (8)

24 Draw the cockney girl in a sleazy bar (6)

26 Twin infants fighting together? (8,2,4)

DOWN

1 Difficulty finding the 500 excess needed before getting to France (7,2,5)

2 Child of a celebrated film star (4)

3 End of the morning number (6)

4 Not able to describe a seaman (8)

5 His French girl starts a number (4)

7 Some sailors' wives seldom found in port (6)

8 Take away what's come up (4,3,7)

12 The bishop might put his head in the joint (5)

14 Give warning that the hothead might bite (5)

16 Shared out in proportion when shelter is put up (8)

18 Shrinks when it could be worse if caught first (6)

21 At last we can see what Reg and Doug have in common (6)

23 Pity it's a girl (4)

25 Not often you see engineers backing the gunners (4)

67

ACROSS

1 Waves of artistic endeavour (8)
5 Dull priest at last coming up with a bit of an idea (6)
9 Another perception of what's needed before the examination (8)
10 Swamp the vessel when there's little time to take the painter first (6)
12 Skill centre at Nunhead where things may get heated (4)
13 Parliamentarian working to see all got rise (10)
15 Make space on board to get ready for action (5,3,5)
19 Went flat out in a testing situation (8,5)
23 Leave salesman backing undertaking (10)
25 In bed at a time when information has to be supplied (4)
28 Cries of triumph – or has there been some mistake? (6)
29 Not mad in becoming assertive (8)
30 What happens when the others have got over the usual extremes (6)
31 Painted looking rather dotty (8)

DOWN

1 He gets involved with risk of getting the bird (6)
2 Vain move to offer a pound for what comes under the hammer (5)
3 Money needed to give the firm a straight start (4)
4 Look round to see one getting on as a developer (7)
6 Try to catch fish with a song (5)
7 Arctic round encompassed by someone you know to be efficient (9)
8 Don't believe in having to stir trouble when there's dirt all around (8)
11 She looks good for a meal (4)
14 Eager to express grief (4)
15 Underground explorer with the sense to see there's plenty of space inside (9)
16 Boy needed to distribute grass (3)
17 Took the plunge in America as a peace activist (4)
18 Person supplying current for people to do a job (8)
20 Take yours and you may have the rest (4)
21 Concern for a watcher (7)
22 Not much money, trade bad, so split up (6)
24 Force to head off simple change (5)
26 Help to gain a victory and do badly (5)

27 Not hard to get along after injury (4)

68

ACROSS

1 They put a twinkle into every part (3-4,4)
9 Educated father of TV finding it wet inside (7)
10 Seamen love to jump clear (7)
11 Take money from what's been handed over to help (3)
12 Reaching a point after getting thinner all round (7)
13 Just a bit of a cut, darling! (7)
14 Decide to be carried in a helicopter (3)
15 Figures provided for the board (5)
17 Search for a way to get clean (5)
18 One alternative (5)
20 Money-making touch when writing about a girl (5)
22 Go out after a rise (3)
24 Seeks food that lasts a long time (7)
25 French resistance capture king and nobleman (7)
26 Tool down for a dance (3)
27 Make contact with merry soul taking cover inside (7)
28 Having a cold run with the ball (7)
29 Get a sniff of what might be going wrong (5,6)

DOWN

1 Though regal in status he could be illegitimate (7,3,5)
2 Nothing put up, nothing taken away in print (7)
3 Going in and out when given the boot finally and laid off (5)
4 Way to the place where ships can anchor (9)
5 Attacks the silly fellow who does badly (7)
6 Figures assembled to get you talking maybe (9,6)
7 Carves up the business of providing property cover (6)
8 The part where the corset gets wrinkled (6)
16 Attacks a bad place to cause a sensation (9)
18 Away to find a cooler place to work (6)
19 Music can be teasing on occasion (7)
21 Getting over the waves or the Internet maybe (7)
23 Some measure of transport that's almost torment (6)
25 Ways of communicating with the Middle East when relief is held up (5)

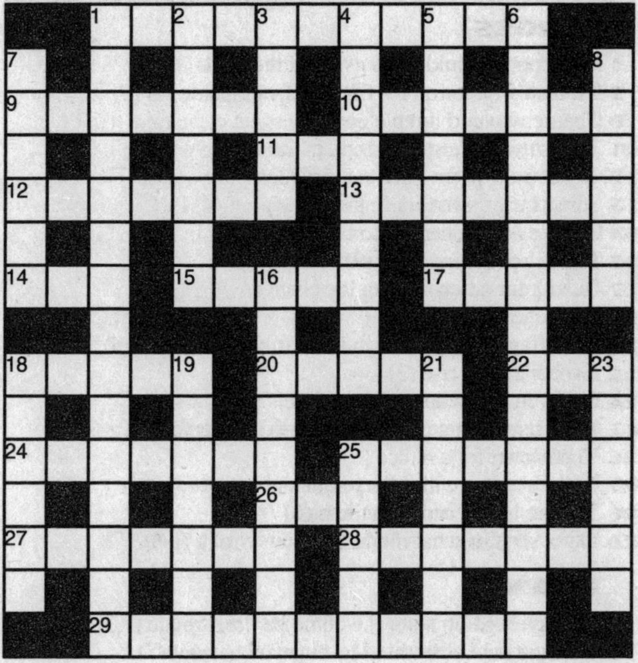
1 2 3 4 5 6
7 8
9 10
11
12 13
14 15 16 17
18 19 20 21 22 23
24 25
26
27 28
29

69

ACROSS

1 Paul moves round the outside of the plant (7)
5 Hit on a way to Express dissatisfaction at work (6)
9 Classic way into giving an impression of being a freak (7)
10 Thin stuff a Welshman took in the wrong way (7)
11 Cry of pain when left by a bird (3)
12 Something underfoot to keep one going (11)
13 One's asked generally to take the anchor in (5)
14 This is something like! (9)
16 Older generation ringing the changes (9)
17 Not believing the old fellow will back a complaint (5)
19 Go different ways here in Paris so the head can get involved (11)
22 Be given an escape when a road is not available (3)
23 Back a supporter to find a place in church for the gospel to be preached (7)
24 It's a man in trouble causing the carry-on (7)
26 Soldier dispatched to the line (6)
27 Expect first signal when about to record a poem (7)

DOWN

1 Ancient hold-up among wolves preventing entry (7)
2 Transport not authorised to move one who can't walk (7,8)
3 She's in a most unfortunate predicament (3)
4 Old Greek upstairs (5)
5 A Swiss hero in the position of a hanger-on (9)
6 Hint at being free to turn right (5)
7 Maintain activity in the dispatch department (4,6,5)
8 Two boys find a customer (6)
12 The way to move into the lead (5)
14 Letters only at first (9)
15 Fruit drink about twopence (5)
16 Move quietly and you'll get the girl an animal (6)
18 One has to be crazy listening to the Colonel describing what's inside (3-4)
20 Bar to gin swilling (5)
21 Cut the ends off a sort of shawl this way (5)
25 Everything that's finished (3)

70

ACROSS

1 Newspaper feature with backbone that gives one some standing? (6,6)
8 Was introduced to the Queen after a morning of current assessment (7)
9 Flier hits back when there's a quarrel (7)
11 Alan's dream destroyed by one said to enjoy a hot time (10)
12 Stuff making a comeback as brandy (4)
14 Pokes fun at standard set by senior citizens without money (8)
16 By itself it represents slow progress (6)
17 Managed to take one from a foreign land (3)
19 Nowhere near to mere chaos (6)
21 Shoddy Russian aircraft returned with a fault (8)
24 Prison opening removed the connection (4)
25 Caning male deviant for evil intent (10)
27 More than one thing (7)
28 Tie a knot at speed – you can say that again! (7)
29 Joined with conditions to see the country (6,6)

DOWN

1 Corresponding with teacher distributing mail internally (7)
2 Some idea of getting a friend round to cause alarm (10)
3 As far as one can go in a posh car when one scores another way (8)
4 Money we have to raise for some nut (6)
5 Go ahead and swing it to evade duty (4)
6 Dram not used as acid (7)
7 Plant found when artists raised a broken pillar in South Africa (12)
10 One might be stumped by his quick action (6-6)
13 Cause bewilderment with music from hell? (10)
15 Get depressed when idle talk arises (3)
18 One doesn't believe in Ulster greeting a number of items (8)
20 Day in the near future bringing rains (7)
22 Girl at a sale scrum gets hot and cold (7)
23 Not allowed in to see a bishop in retirement (6)
26 Attempt at getting killed (4)

71

ACROSS

6 The same two children (9,5)
9 Make little of a psychiatrist (6)
10 Ruth goes round city and river as a matter of immediate concern (8)
11 Crop-free, wild by necessity (8)
13 Straighten out what's remarkable to the Scot and the Italian (6)
15 Country writer (6)
17 Ask to cover half the capital and feel at home (6)
19 Damaged gun all right inside (6)
20 Drawing wagon back into turning (8)
22 One gives support in a sticky situation (8)
24 One's got it in the neck for being an untidy person (6)
26 One doesn't know what one's doing in it (8,6)

DOWN

1 He backs the Queen for twenty pounds (7,7)
2 Fairy being soft when anger rises (4)
3 He makes things hot for a city on a river (6)
4 Something to be gained by taking flight (8)
5 Sheepish creature taken right into jug (4)
7 Given international cover at a high level (6)
8 Zero response when a bid is made without resources (7,2,5)
12 He has a name for being blunt (5)
14 Striking example of personal influence (5)
16 Colourful contribution to the outcome of a wedding (8)
18 Cast it off without making a move (6)
21 Diverting a bus on the way makes no sense (6)
23 Bird man – no way! (4)
25 Call for a token of personal commitment (4)

ACROSS

1 Novelist able to turn over into mad poet (8)
5 Coax a little woman into ruffled lace (6)
9 Dealer in literary thrills (8)
10 The way to upset a setter (6)
12 Growth of Welsh nationalism (4)
13 Swilling rum, it's Aunt who makes a bloomer (10)
15 Tree creature of some sense making an old joke (5,8)
19 Polite name for peerage issue (8,5)
23 Corner where you can get a proper view (5,5)
25 You can have one in stitches (4)
28 Type inclined to give stress (6)
29 Firm about Red trouble-making (8)
30 Be comfortable at home with some of what's left (6)
31 One may be surprised to have them raised (8)

DOWN

1 Get to grips with the gear (6)
2 Speak of nothing but what you get paid (5)
3 Female youth leader taking a boy over (4)
4 Publicity needed to make happy churchman (7)
6 Where one may be led to form a union (5)
7 Basis for lying that is in time past submission (9)
8 Guess ties have been knotted by a friend (8)
11 The thing that gives a companion irritation (4)
14 Worry when the lady leaves a stream of water (4)
15 Get sort of rough with a girl – it's a matter of timing (4-5)
16 Shrinking company (3)
17 Be pictured with Wren's almost final building plot (4)
18 Contempt expressed about the un-American religious has a sting in the tail (8)
20 Go down to find something in the kitchen (4)
21 Gangling youth with drawers (7)
22 They are still smouldering at the end of three months (6)
24 The devious tailor loses nothing in this case (5)
26 Time to muse (5)
27 Dirt thrown up but at first saying nothing (4)

ACROSS

1 Good mates in the same business? (4,7)
9 Lively enough to get out of bed (7)
10 Luring half-heartedly into taking brief employment (7)
11 Big loss of good colour (3)
12 Just a bit peculiar? (7)
13 Brave relation of a Socialist (7)
14 Stolen out of the oven? (3)
15 Accommodation for some of those degenerate peers (5)
17 Get over feeling angry (5)
18 Think about all those children (5)
20 Chose work with father in TV (5)
22 Let the head be inclined to be agreeable (3)
24 Abandon authority (7)
25 One charges a couple of hundred to the employer (7)
26 Game to offer a racing tip (3)
27 Vera has difficulty getting a man put off (7)
28 Silver circulating having hit bottom (7)
29 Silently performs the capture of a rodent – wrong for this day and age (6,5)

DOWN

1 Best basis for making up (10,5)
2 Object when having to appear in torn dress (7)
3 Struggle for the last tramcar out of fear (5)
4 Put a word in when I, a Parisian, get taken to court after one rent dispute (9)
5 Crazy to be tossing coin around when on the move (7)
6 Obstinately refuse to give up a personal firearms collection (5,2,4,4)
7 Ornamentation that gets a grip (6)
8 They represent a possible convenience (6)
16 Demonstrated the German ability to produce food (9)
18 Everything that goes into rotten song (6)
19 Meant to see weight-lifting in action (7)
21 Good manners requires one to be beaten when an Italian writer comes in (7)
23 Consider ideas of politicians to mock going in (6)
25 A bit out of the general run (5)

ACROSS

1 Enforcer of regulations taking half the team from a bodyguard (7)
5 Struggle to get a doctor into a jacket (6)
9 Aim to get a majority in an extreme situation (7)
10 Such sports as are given no coverage? (7)
11 Last character with spectacles in the beastly place (3)
12 Without feeling unfriendly when initiated (4-7)
13 One expects to be inside a long time (5)
14 Pray sails can be re-rigged when you can't move (9)
16 Went again to see if given a new look outside (9)
17 A gentleman in India has retreated before the International Brigade (5)
19 Being upwardly mobile might make one ruminate (11)
22 The man who chooses the right girl (3)
23 Well known to have caught some of them in enterprising ways (7)
24 Article in the home displaying taste (7)
26 Feverish cold after the fellow gets caught with one (6)
27 Forced to give one a thousand when the question is put (7)

DOWN

1 Take the biscuit for getting knotted (7)
2 Loved one to be thought more likely to win than not (4-2,9)
3 Excessively short in the tooth (3)
4 Gunners allowed to raise an animal (5)
5 Much struck by being given something to wear (9)
6 Something to be said for giving the Frenchman a name (5)
7 Having achieved peaks of venerability (2,3,2,3,5)
8 Inclines to award ranks (6)
12 Worries in a fright from first to last (5)
14 Loving the country the old man takes three on credit mostly (9)
15 Not one likely to succeed in other roles (5)
16 Given something of a battering by the beast over the water (6)
18 Don't admit a girl to be the one providing the drinks (7)
20 Water running right into the shelter (5)
21 End of poem in a now long-forgotten voice (5)
25 Fix up to have a quick drink (3)

ACROSS

1 Self-important sailor having got a shore job? (4-2-6)
8 Gasp about the time taken to make a show (7)
9 A broken leg needs support according to calculations (7)
11 One talks a lot about that mad character on television (10)
12 Not heading for the races, Mac? (4)
14 Excitement at a hanging? (8)
16 Ring again to cancel (6)
17 Politician lacking nothing in effort (3)
19 Reveal man's confusion in the country (6)
21 In a wild estate he is one to appreciate beauty (8)
24 Achieved a comeback with a classic garment (4)
25 Ferry often wrecked by too much boldness (10)
27 Start losing work nearby and get put inside (7)
28 Cut off one that will be very critical about nothing (7)
29 Pass over those seen to be discerning (5-7)

DOWN

1 Cuts after a dance may be puzzling (7)
2 Plan to make another application for something to drink (10)
3 Saving virtue of relieving boredom (8)
4 One speaks of a rotor as going round (6)
5 Small bodies of fruit (4)
6 Somewhere to sleep where the young can get free of lice (7)
7 Area closed until let out for a long-distance traveller (5,7)
10 People with guns in term really can get a break (12)
13 Making a show of getting started (7,3)
15 Time expressed in general terms (3)
18 Not an old horse spending time on the heather (8)
20 Marvellous silver found in new claim (7)
22 Mere lad corrupted by Beryl (7)
23 Away with hesitations in making bids (6)
26 It may weaken the spirit (4)

76

ACROSS

6 Covered with blood, couples can be put right (7,7)
9 Draw a vessel to a point (6)
10 Musical get-together (8)
11 Left high and dry in a London street (8)
13 Hurried back with a line offering little scope (6)
15 No stranger to the oyster bed (6)
17 Near the time to start needing a private room (6)
19 In the past Raleigh was one of the stars (6)
20 Fair cart on the way round might give you a lift (8)
22 Anything in the German issue? (8)
24 The fellow gains nothing in an attempt at speculation (6)
26 Mind making some moves? (6,8)

DOWN

1 They could be helpful in seaside digs (6,3,5)
2 Passage of mine in the great tradition (4)
3 Flower found to have died after the choir outing (6)
4 Wild Pearl's on the offensive (8)
5 Feeling friendly by the fire (4)
7 Finished with the party that has to exaggerate (6)
8 Disallow the use of a lure (4,3,2,5)
12 One has to do something at some stage (5)
14 It's a step up if one doesn't stay in bed (5)
16 Book with a cover that may soon be changed (8)
18 Master sound devices to form a mould (6)
21 Leave work and go to bed (6)
23 Get a new look at the opening (4)
25 Unrecorded rise of no merit (4)

77

ACROSS

1 Urge changes a number found horrible (8)
5 Little time to get back by public transport if a cloud threatens rain (6)
9 Call up a crowd to one with awful lies (8)
10 Money back if it curdles the milk (6)
12 No company person has been given a pound (4)
13 Secure phone for one seeking illegal gain (4-6)
15 On the shortest route, honest! (5,8)
19 In pursuit of style somehow (5,1,7)
23 Put too much on top and get badly burned (10)
25 Look like a somebody superior (4)
28 First blood in test of some people (6)
29 Make an effort to slug Gert in wrestling (8)
30 Research set out for you to take in (6)
31 Sign of Turkish power increasing (8)

DOWN

1 Get a pound up in play when you take chances (6)
2 Not entirely sophisticated view of the city (5)
3 The stuff of superior advocacy (4)
4 Compelled to lead a nag – sorry, horse! (7)
6 Thought Labour's leader to be perfect (5)
7 Fashionable movement with musical comedian aboard (9)
8 Steep way to give us a treat (8)
11 Abandoned on the side (4)
14 Bar put up for one who isn't honest (4)
15 Getting the idea of an assembly (9)
16 Perhaps suffering a final setback in the spring (3)
17 Sharp as a lot of detectives might be (4)
18 Frolicked in a way that drove cat wild (8)
20 Strong point made on behalf of first-timer (4)
21 Little in the rest of a dance could be more pleasant (7)
22 Pressing a respectable person to carry on at our end (6)
24 Money for the band (5)
26 Wild gale on the way for a flier (5)
27 Agitation to get some backing in banning animal's suffering (4)

1
2
3
4
5
6
7
8
9
10
11
12
13
14
15
16
17
18
19
20
21
22
23
24
25
26
27
28
29
30
31

ACROSS

1 Repeatedly making a dozen deliveries (4,3,4)
9 Openings for the viewer with permits (7)
10 Hampered by wooden shoes (7)
11 She doesn't see it in the film (3)
12 Most righteous anger quick to get around (7)
13 Ale left out when the bill is presented (7)
14 All those performances have to be quick (3)
15 Object of an obsession (5)
17 What's wrong with having no time for fear? (5)
18 Support one in a low voice (5)
20 It's a pleasure to be in the leisure centre at lunch-time (5)
22 No sense offering a non-standard repeater (3)
24 Runner becoming a pest (7)
25 Country cover (7)
26 Low humour but not dead (3)
27 Restrain journalist getting some sleep outside (7)
28 Wet cloth clinging round one in a pub (7)
29 Hint uttered obscurely to reverse the flow (4,3,4)

DOWN

1 Your correspondent, Sir, will provide help as instructed (8,7)
2 Something essential in the heater maybe (7)
3 Investment rising to be something worth having (5)
4 Religious rules expected to cover expert coming up with a record (9)
5 Five to ten is past the time break (7)
6 Soldier training as a matter of habit (7,8)
7 Man to fire wrong young beast (6)
8 Top person – on paper (6)
16 Lose a point and loss of freedom is the final put-down (9)
18 Ambassador invested in most superior order (6)
19 Adherent of public communication (7)
21 Time at school in one achieves certain ends (7)
23 Not looking right to Hugh, however (6)
25 Code for giving extra when you find a way in (5)

79

ACROSS

1 Saved from crude distortion about directions (7)
5 One might cover shopping for a rotter in a backward time (6)
9 It reminds me to follow the soldiers (7)
10 Do well to put the bus terminal right outside (7)
11 Begin to lose the way when trickery is revealed (3)
12 One takes fruit on the water in India (11)
13 It's going to be material, one might say (5)
14 Frenchman taking a girl to be one of five must be a dummy (9)
16 It all adds up to a lot of concrete possibly (9)
17 Has a look at the prospects (5)
19 Society record for getting things going (11)
22 Poetry not yet given its due, so to speak (3)
23 Unknown member of the team or someone else? (7)
24 South African party in depression when drapery is short (7)
26 Relative shortage providing publicity for the nude (6)
27 Not strictly solo going around the city (7)

DOWN

1 Push and puff when out of control (7)
2 Bus or train might give you a clue (9,2,2,2)
3 Vessel you could take for part of the journey (3)
4 Go under the medical adviser you have (5)
5 Ian break into a fruit machine (9)
6 Material provided by the clergy (5)
7 One may get high on leaving here (9,6)
8 It enables one to draw something deceptive about the light (6)
12 Beat beans or peas (5)
14 Need dream interpretation to show one didn't go straight (9)
15 Goes away without having left hangovers (5)
16 Attraction of a very cheap ring (6)
18 Cry seen to be out of place on stage maybe (7)
20 Woman from the time before the last (5)
21 Victory secured by a man in a book (5)
25 Invitation to see about first English sign (3)

80

ACROSS

1 Player associated with river in two-way movement (4,3,5)
8 Take back what you said about the land (7)
9 It's his turn to go on stream and shine (7)
11 Hair about to finish in pursuit of style (10)
12 Indication that you can make a name for yourself (4)
14 Give direction to Alec and Ian's wanderings (8)
16 German capital and French cover (6)
17 Food from somewhere in Northamptonshire (3)
19 One spends time in writing when pictures are needed (6)
21 Getting involved with using a rod when most of the net's gone (8)
24 Fellow with cracked skin (4)
25 Steward with exclusive functions (7-3)
27 An old queen gives one real embarrassment (7)
28 Tricky lady hiding return travel permit (7)
29 See and forget to turn and move unwillingly (4,4,4)

DOWN

1 One's neither here nor there in this (7)
2 Handle rice distribution when there's a light hold-up (10)
3 Surprise when the villa is getting hot (8)
4 Humble place to lie up when the sea is rough (6)
5 Turnover therefore amounting to a frightening figure (4)
6 Training needed to move out in it (7)
7 Mad critic on a bender finishing an article about the North (6,6)
10 Be consistent on the scaffold? (4,8)
13 Gather in church (10)
15 Deal with the intake (3)
18 They demonstrate what the lady has to force up on top (8)
20 Claim to be a true reform for the unpaid (7)
22 One uses mockery that appears hard at first (7)
23 Person responsible for dead take-overs (6)
26 Arms raised to get comfortable (4)

81

ACROSS

6 Band surrounded by drums maybe will get a personal hearing (4,2,4,4)

9 Head off that man when deep trouble will make progress difficult (6)

10 Mystery of bad speller's identity (8)

11 Being in a wound dressing one goes up the wall (8)

13 Grumble about the deal maybe (6)

15 Success of the cause (6)

17 I'm first, you're second (6)

19 Dog of mine losing the line (6)

20 Spy bears dancing – but one doesn't mean to stop (6-2)

22 Pay out money with no enjoyment when bruises take a bad turn (8)

24 Big house occupant actually taking some back for a rest (6)

26 It's a gift for those who have joined (7,7)

DOWN

1 Team transfer making erratic progress? (4,4,2,4)

2 She can take over without getting cross (4)

3 Mum is brought up to be advanced (6)

4 Option about direction you can take (8)

5 Food offered by people getting to you at last (4)

7 Way to make progress as a nurse (6)

8 Best of all, she looks like a queen (8,6)

12 Permitted not to start being bad (5)

14 Too sticky to have real sparkle? (5)

16 Loud approval for her nice dance at midnight (8)

18 Support needed to prevent falling behind? (6)

21 Place for an eye? You can put a plug in it (6)

23 Person who might be dead (4)

25 Not now included in Southend United football team (4)

82

ACROSS

1 Run after rotten case of meat (8)
5 Drop off the board finally with possibly worse to come (6)
9 Be protective of a pound by giving informal cover (8)
10 One might take your arm (6)
12 Get carried away by some superior idea (4)
13 Making progress towards a get-together (10)
15 They are the making of real people (5,3,5)
19 It was worn for a time in the past (6,7)
23 Not going straight for a fair attraction (10)
25 Don't go on driving in open land (4)
28 Nothing can be made clear by a prophet (6)
29 African regalia altered at some point (8)
30 One tries to find a place for bishop, king and queen (6)
31 My tumble with Rupert isn't worth much (8)

DOWN

1 Motherless girl has to sound harsh to get on board (6)
2 Specified the need for it in the month coming up (5)
3 See the way to become a superior person (4)
4 Piping of a sanctimonious sibling going to church (7)
6 Someone at the top to keep things straight (5)
7 We who possess nothing ask a person looking miserable (9)
8 Happening to die out as it gets dark (8)
11 Somewhere warm in the hinterland of Provence (4)
14 The book's about him giving the lady a ring (4)
15 Lucky outcome of an utter disaster (9)
16 Loving to call out and make a fuss (3)
17 Not happy about looking cold (4)
18 Falso incentive to accumulate debts (8)
20 Something sugary with six faces (4)
21 Brave wife and nobleman both failing to end decay (7)
22 Having a thin time in the South relative to New York (6)
24 Go into digs (5)
26 Waving a veil to show one's cheerful (5)
27 Give a big smile of support (4)

ACROSS

1 It makes up for being an actor (6,5)
9 Possibly not a city but a province (7)
10 Determine to find the answer again (7)
11 One's stupid to hang about without money (3)
12 Threatened to get better one inside (7)
13 Nil movement in the flat – wake up! (7)
14 One thing and another (3)
15 Get the bird for some of those Greta Garbo impersonations (5)
17 Is among the last of the children to have got out of bed (5)
18 Making some sort of row is no good if you haven't the right (5)
20 Being governed by depression (5)
22 Take in sailors leaving to see the world (3)
24 Bird in the country or some of it (7)
25 Given such heat treatment as to make a difference in colour (7)
26 She's given a greeting on retirement (3)
27 Away to see the drop where water emerges (7)
28 Digital protection for the limb that's broken (7)
29 Language prepared to give a person plenty to say (5,6)

DOWN

1 Have trouble taking a bath? (3,4,3,5)
2 It might make painful listening (7)
3 Nothing in a fellow's upbringing covers hair (5)
4 Carried out quite rightly (9)
5 Looking inward when there's water all round? (7)
6 Support for home entertainment (10,5)
7 Pledge medal to one in bed (6)
8 Continue writing about Northern flier (6)
16 RAF marking agreed in song (9)
18 Strike build-up over work (6)
19 Spin and a rag in Spain (7)
21 Studying at university (7)
23 Move with time to plan spending (6)
25 Proportion of theatre work open to be removed (5)

ACROSS

1 Money put down is back in the warehouse (7)
5 Plays for time in the theatre (6)
9 One in the garden is angry when disturbed (7)
10 Having outstanding points of a thin kind (7)
11 Heavenly atmosphere (3)
12 Happy to see ten going to American in dispute (11)
13 Bert's wrong about one lot of families (5)
14 Soon to introduce a respectable woman with no publicity (9)
16 Bring in a little creature of some significance (9)
17 Female in prison not fighting for cover (5)
19 Producer of some earth-shaking records (11)
22 Entertain the departing man with drink (3)
23 Something from the paper that's quite sharp (7)
24 Take the end off in secrecy (7)
26 One's never to be a slave (6)
27 Tried to get an animal back when seen going around (7)

DOWN

1 Far from being friendly (7)
2 One's able to provide personal representation (8,7)
3 Student rising making things hot (3)
4 More than one writer (5)
5 Account of a speech that might be made (9)
6 Informal talk of having to move pictures around (5)
7 Flower girl in depressed circumstances (4,2,3,6)
8 In a bad temper about baking well done? (6)
12 Jump over to get out of trouble (5)
14 Grouse at time taken in Grampian excursion (9)
15 Respected figure in a tree (5)
16 A little one makes the nicest stew (6)
18 Showed anger at having to view the dead (7)
20 Being a bit wet one is in the majority (5)
21 Gratitude expressed for having set out a sample (5)
25 Not all systems go in Germany (3)

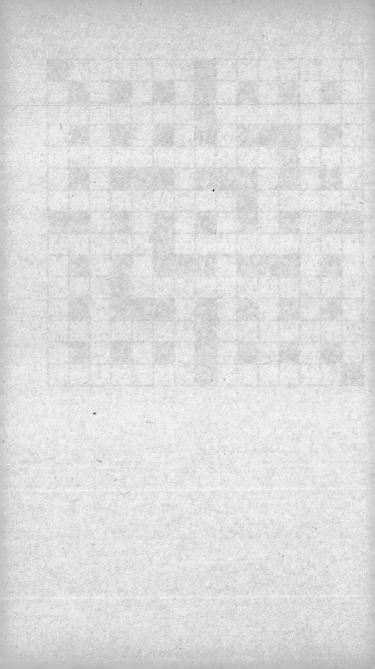

Solutions

1

ACROSS: 1 Gallant, **5** Splash, **9** Rightly, **10** Natural, **11** Act, **12** Kitchenette, **13** Drive, **14** Aldershot, **16** Regulates, **17** Punch, **19** Anticipated, **22** Sip, **23** Eminent, **24** Relieve, **26** Vestry, **27** Exposes.
DOWN: 1 Garland, **2** Lightning strike, **3** Apt, **4** Tryst, **5** Sun-shades, **6** Latin, **7** Stretch one's legs, **8** Albert, **12** Knell, **14** Antipathy, **15** Rapid, **16** Reader, **18** Hapless, **20** Chest, **21** Three, **25** Lap.

2

ACROSS: 1 Ugly duckling, **8** Errands, **9** Pursuer, **11** High-fliers, **12** Wind, **14** Outclass, **16** Bishop, **17** Top, **19** Eggnog, **21** Waterloo, **24** Epic, **25** Tweedledum, **27** Travail, **28** Tintern, **29** Nevertheless.
DOWN: 1 Upright, **2** Longfellow, **3** Dustiest, **4** Capers, **5** Lark, **6** Nourish, **7** Dethronement, **10** Redeployment, **13** Side-glance, **15** Sow, **18** Patentee, **20** Grimace, **22** Ladders, **23** Twilit, **26** Bare.

3

ACROSS: 6 On the other hand, **9** Escape, **10** Recruits, **11** Educated, **13** Affair, **15** Thrash, **17** Strong, **19** Actual, **20** Arcadian, **22** Dictator, **24** Parent, **26** Sealed envelope.
DOWN: 1 House detective, **2** Etna, **3** Select, **4** Merchant, **5** Thou, **7** Tirade, **8** Nothing daunted, **12** Corfu, **14** Flood, **16** Solitude, **18** Barren, **21** Copper, **23** Toll, **25** Room.

4

ACROSS: 1 Dip-stick, **5** Gaffer, **9** Compound, **10** Fabric, **12** Dish, **13** Meddlesome, **15** Capital letter, **19** Businesswoman, **23** Rain-forest, **25** Stop, **28** Earwig, **29** Palisade, **30** Noddle, **31** Sentence.
DOWN: 1 Decode, **2** Pumps, **3** Trot, **4** Consent, **6** Amaze, **7** Forgotten, **8** Rocketry, **11** Idol, **14** Spin, **15** Cashiered, **16** Ass, **17** Emma, **18** Aberdeen, **20** Surf, **21** Wastage, **22** Sphere, **24** Frill, **26** Twain, **27** Lift.

5

ACROSS: 1 Betting shop, **9** Arrange, **10** Impasse, **11** Nil, **12** Unhorse, **13** Litotes, **14** Era, **15** Locum, **17** Reedy, **18** Pop-up, **20** Extra, **22** Alb, **24** Sceptic, **25** Kestrel, **26** Eye, **27** Iberian, **28** Borough, **29** Take on board.
DOWN: 1 Birthday present, **2** Tendril, **3** Irene, **4** Guillemot, **5** Hipster, **6** Pass the hat round, **7** Salute, **8** Jersey, **16** Crescendo, **18** Pastis, **19** Patrick, **21** Austria, **23** Bolshy, **25** Kebab.

6

ACROSS: 1 Upstart, **5** Rattle, **9** Dragnet, **10** Creator, **11** Rap, **12** Parenthesis, **13** Offal, **14** Privation, **16** Expensive, **17** Giver, **19** Certificate, **22** Nag, **23** Revenge, **24** Russian, **26** Cloche, **27** Sternly.

DOWN: 1 Undergo, **2** Stamp of approval, **3** Ann, **4** Tutor, **5** Recondite, **6** Teeth, **7** Latest invention, **8** Prison, **12** Pylon, **14** Privilege, **15** Argue, **16** Escort, **18** Regency, **20** Ionic, **21** Arras, **25** She.

7

ACROSS: 1 Approach road, **8** Obscure, **9** Medical, **11** Disconcert, **12** Turn, **14** Mistrust, **16** Quoted, **17** Tag, **19** Abject, **21** Palmists, **24** Isle, **25** Salmonella, **27** Neither, **28** Totemic, **29** By comparison.

DOWN: 1 Assists, **2** Plutocracy, **3** Overcast, **4** Camera, **5** Rude, **6** Account, **7** Condemnation, **10** Long-distance, **13** Culminates, **15** Tap, **18** Gas-meter, **20** Jollity, **22** Solomon, **23** Satrap, **26** Shoo.

8

ACROSS: 6 Nasty bit of work, **9** Stroll, **10** Fragment, **11** Intruder, **13** Disown, **15** Defeat, **17** Dreamy, **19** Asleep, **20** Floodlit, **22** Dispense, **24** Tomato, **26** Decisive factor.

DOWN: 1 Instant dislike, **2** Oslo, **3** Eyelid, **4** Colander, **5** Swim, **7** Infirm, **8** Runaway victory, **12** Rifle, **14** Stand, **16** Appendix, **18** Effete, **21** Outlay, **23** Pail, **25** Mite.

9

ACROSS: 1 Transept, **5** Ground, **9** Terminal, **10** Strips, **12** Ewer, **13** Charioteer, **15** Words and music, **19** Root of all evil, **23** Freeloader, **25** Plea, **28** Ironic, **29** Manifest, **30** Grease, **31** Adultery.

DOWN: 1 Totter, **2** Agree, **3** Slip, **4** Peaches, **6** Ratio, **7** Universal, **8** District, **11** Bran, **14** Brio, **15** Wholesome, **16** All, **17** Move, **18** Trifling, **20** Alas, **21** Leeward, **22** Pantry, **24** Lairs, **26** Liege, **27** Pill.

10

ACROSS: 1 Flat refusal, **9** Miracle, **10** Arbiter, **11** Keg, **12** Ditches, **13** Elected, **14** Eel, **15** Local, **17** Tally, **18** Aesop, **20** Rated, **22** Hat, **24** Dispose, **25** Spinner, **26** Net, **27** Nearest, **28** Outcome, **29** Party spirit.

DOWN: 1 First-class stamp, **2** Alcohol, **3** Reeks, **4** Flageolet, **5** Subject, **6** Let it all hang out, **7** Smudge, **8** Friday, **16** Carpentry, **18** Ardent, **19** Pioneer, **21** Drifter, **23** Turner, **25** Stoop.

11

ACROSS: 1 Costard, **5** Debate, **9** Wassall, **10** Patella, **11** Lie, **12** Glass-blower, **13** Pater, **14** Patrolmen, **16** Protester, **17** Dread, **19** Salaciously, **22** Arm, **23** Allheal, **24** Cutlass, **26** Oyster, **27** Strange.
DOWN: 1 Cowslip, **2** Suspect foul play, **3** Aga, **4** Delia, **5** Depositor, **6** Betel, **7** Till we meet again, **8** Matron, **12** Gorse, **14** Pot-boiler, **15** Oddly, **16** Pascal, **18** Demesne, **20** Crest, **21** Socks, **25** Tar.

12

ACROSS: 1 Second chance, **8** Learner, **9** Lantern, **11** Temperance, **12** Pair, **14** Perished, **16** Adhere, **17** Sit, **19** Action, **21** Monarchy, **24** Foul, **25** Free speech, **27** Retract, **28** Anagram, **29** Herbal remedy.
DOWN: 1 Stammer, **2** Conversion, **3** Narrates, **4** Calico, **5** Aunt, **6** Cremate, **7** All to play for, **10** Nursery rhyme, **13** Ideal place, **15** Dim, **18** Tolerate, **20** Trustee, **22** Clearly, **23** Brutal, **26** Barb.

13

ACROSS: 6 Editorial staff, **9** Angler, **10** Playbill, **11** Rescuers, **13** Hector, **15** Throne, **17** Advice, **19** Gallon, **20** Chaplain, **22** Improver, **24** Crowds, **26** Ancient history.
DOWN: 1 Neanderthal man, **2** Will, **3** Course, **4** Bleached, **5** Stub, **7** Impose, **8** Fall on evil days, **12** Coral, **14** Chill, **16** Non-event, **18** Scorch, **21** Accuse, **23** Raid, **25** Oboe.

14

ACROSS: 1 Business end, **9** Secured, **10** Example, **11** Ill, **12** Elector, **13** Distort, **14** Two, **15** Mocha, **17** Diary, **18** Resin, **20** Treat, **22** Imp, **24** Crucial, **25** Rubicon, **26** One, **27** Nothing, **28** Buckram, **29** No great loss.
DOWN: 1 Bachelor's button, **2** Stratum, **3** Nadir, **4** Sheldrake, **5** Elapsed, **6** Diplomatic corps, **7** Assent, **8** Sentry, **16** Catalogue, **18** Recant, **19** Nailing, **21** Tobacco, **23** Panama, **25** Rebut.

15

ACROSS: 1 Insipid, **5** Adjust, **9** Shorten, **10** Teacher, **11** Egg, **12** Cornerstone, **13** Dense, **14** Matrimony, **16** Pragmatic, **17** Otter, **19** Cartography, **22** Owl, **23** Italics, **24** Insight, **26** Aeneas, **27** Exerted.
DOWN: 1 Instead, **2** Shotgun marriage, **3** Pet, **4** Diner, **5** Authentic, **6** Jeans, **7** School of thought, **8** Artery, **12** Cream, **14** Motorists, **15** Ivory, **16** Picnic, **18** Related, **20** Olive, **21** Pride, **25** Sue.

16

ACROSS: 1 Cash and carry, **8** Useless, **9** Traitor, **11** Gothic arch, **12** Onus, **14** Achilles, **16** Cicada, **17** Sum, **19** Almost, **21** Baptised, **24** Anna, **25** Balderdash, **27** Mariner, **28** Ruction, **29** Stretch nylon.
DOWN: 1 Cheetah, **2** Specialist, **3** Assuages, **4** Detach, **5** Adam, **6** Rotunda, **7** Burglar alarm, **10** Rise and shine, **13** Historical, **15** Sub, **18** Mandarin, **20** Minaret, **22** Station, **23** Fabric, **26** Knee.

17

ACROSS: 6 Honeymoon hotel, **9** Domino, **10** Frontage, **11** Compress, **13** Muslim, **15** Tragic, **17** Trough, **19** Method, **20** Corniche, **22** Dialogue, **24** Divine, **26** Vending machine.
DOWN: 1 Throw of the dice, **2** Anti, **3** Bygone, **4** Informer, **5** Boot, **7** Oafish, **8** English Channel, **12** Poach, **14** Saudi, **16** Indigent, **18** Scream, **21** Reduce, **23** Lido, **25** Vain.

18

ACROSS: 1 Desolate, **5** Campus, **9** Rosemary, **10** Citric, **12** Cone, **13** Ceremonial, **15** Maid of all work, **19** Sitting pretty, **23** Opera house, **25** Must, **28** Inward, **29** Division, **30** Hither, **31** Destined.
DOWN: 1 Direct, **2** Susan, **3** Lump, **4** Torpedo, **6** Amigo, **7** Parsimony, **8** Suchlike, **11** Hera, **14** Mimi, **15** Mother-wit, **16** Fop, **17** Late, **18** Astonish, **20** Goon, **21** Respite, **22** Stoned, **24** Agree, **26** Union, **27** Mint.

19

ACROSS: 1 Adhesive tape, **8** Incense, **9** Surplus, **11** Intimation, **12** Knee, **14** Archives, **16** Fourth, **17** Dug, **19** Yankee, **21** Baptists, **24** Arum, **25** Accounting, **27** Drifter, **28** Thicket, **29** Cherry brandy.
DOWN: 1 Ascetic, **2** Handmaiden, **3** Sheathed, **4** Vision, **5** Tart, **6** Pilsner, **7** Military band, **10** See the sights, **13** Contention, **15** Sub, **18** Garotter, **20** Nourish, **22** Slickly, **23** Scurvy, **26** Star.

20

ACROSS: 1 Compact disc, **9** Matador, **10** Stirrup, **11** Elm, **12** Scholar, **13** Asinine, **14** Don, **15** Rabbi, **17** Lager, **18** Sun-up, **20** Owner, **22** Ash, **24** Rip-cord, **25** Scandal, **26** Sap, **27** Swinish, **28** Elegant, **29** Ghost-writer.
DOWN: 1 Catch one napping, **2** Meddler, **3** Airer, **4** Tasmanian, **5** Initial, **6** Carriage and pair, **7** Amused, **8** Appear, **16** Bloodshot, **18** Stress, **19** Proviso, **21** Reagent, **23** Helots, **25** Spear.

21

ACROSS: 1 Segment, **5** Caress, **9** Annabel, **10** Nominal, **11** Par, **12** Tediousness, **13** Ruler, **14** Furnished, **16** Percolate, **17** Foyer, **19** Accumulator, **22** Aim, **23** Nairobi, **24** Asunder, **26** Recess, **27** Trestle.
DOWN: 1 Scamper, **2** General practice, **3** Ebb, **4** Tiled, **5** Concourse, **6** Remus, **7** Since the year dot, **8** Closed, **12** Torso, **14** Frailties, **15** Infer, **16** Plaint, **18** Remorse, **20** Moose, **21** Toast, **25** Use.

22

ACROSS: 1 April showers, **8** Auction, **9** Servant, **11** Stepfather, **12** Wind, **14** Pastries, **16** Pronto, **17** Nod, **19** Outset, **21** Winnable, **24** Hard, **25** Invalidate, **27** Thistle, **28** Transit, **29** Problem child.
DOWN: 1 Archers, **2** Reinforced, **3** Lengthen, **4** Hasten, **5** Worm, **6** Realign, **7** False prophet, **10** Tide of events, **13** Frangipani, **15** Sow, **18** Didactic, **20** Terrier, **22** Braised, **23** Sneeze, **26** Stab.

23

ACROSS: 6 Loaded question, **9** Scrape, **10** Infinite, **11** Dramatic, **13** Rubber, **15** Charms, **17** Depict, **19** Butter, **20** Accorded, **22** Stitches, **24** Excess, **26** Breakneck speed.
DOWN: 1 Electric guitar, **2** Gala, **3** Defect, **4** Perforce, **5** Eton, **7** Quince, **8** On the other side, **12** Meant, **14** Brier, **16** Merchant, **18** Barsac, **21** Crease, **23** Trap, **25** Crew.

24

ACROSS: 1 Half-back, **5** Hawser, **9** Allegory, **10** Potion, **12** Tick, **13** Avalanches, **15** Draining-board, **19** Exchange blows, **23** Obligation, **25** Seal, **28** Regain, **29** Disallow, **30** Energy, **31** Berliner.
DOWN: 1 Hearth, **2** Lilac, **3** Bags, **4** Caravan, **6** Acorn, **7** Skinheads, **8** Ringside, **11** Plan, **14** Lama, **15** Decalogue, **16** Ire, **17** Book, **18** Resource, **20** Gath, **21** Bromide, **22** Flower, **24** Going, **26** Ellen, **27** Mall.

25

ACROSS: 1 First to last, **9** Tank top, **10** Tax-free, **11** Sea, **12** Fantasy, **13** Grovels, **14** Ali, **15** Elfin, **17** Spite, **18** Tulle, **20** Orlop, **22** Cab, **24** Uniform, **25** Sponsor, **26** Awl, **27** Brazier, **28** Ovation, **29** Dutch cheese.
DOWN: 1 Financial wizard, **2** Rat race, **3** Tipsy, **4** Octagonal, **5** Anxious, **6** Three-piece suite, **7** Staffa, **8** Lessee, **16** Frog-march, **18** Thumbs, **19** Egotist, **21** Probate, **23** Boring, **25** Sloth.

26

ACROSS: 1 Postman, **5** Dictum, **9** Sleight, **10** Soulful, **11** Ash, **12** Puss in Boots, **13** Extra, **14** Sheepskin, **16** Adornment, **17** Rider, **19** Deceptively, **22** Rap, **23** Conceal, **24** Relieve, **26** Poetry, **27** Rotates.
DOWN: 1 Passage, **2** See what you can do, **3** Mug, **4** Notes, **5** Dissident, **6** Crumb, **7** Unfrocked priest, **8** Alison, **12** Prawn, **14** Specially, **15** Parry, **16** Addict, **18** Repress, **20** Pleat, **21** Error, **25** Lot.

27

ACROSS: 1 Resettlement, **8** Rummage, **9** Emerald, **11** Vintage car, **12** Hair, **14** Twenties, **16** Legacy, **17** Dad, **19** Mighty, **21** Deputise, **24** Anew, **25** Disappoint, **27** Selfish, **28** Emirate, **29** Incompetence.
DOWN: 1 Romance, **2** Stalactite, **3** Teetered, **4** Leeway, **5** Meet, **6** Niagara, **7** Private means, **10** Dirty weather, **13** Resumption, **15** Sad, **18** Decadent, **20** Gremlin, **22** Imitate, **23** Bishop, **26** Giro.

28

ACROSS: 6 Catherine wheel, **9** Purple, **10** Flattery, **11** Radiator, **13** Tiptoe, **15** Import, **17** Broach, **19** Mental, **20** Heritage, **22** Cardigan, **24** Pastor, **26** Self-possession.
DOWN: 1 Accusative case, **2** Stop, **3** Repeat, **4** Decanter, **5** Shot, **7** Infirm, **8** Ear to the ground, **12** Input, **14** Plant, **16** Religion, **18** Whines, **21** Repast, **23** Deft, **25** Skim.

29

ACROSS: 1 Distrait, **5** Instep, **9** Paradise, **10** Edward, **12** Even, **13** Comparison, **15** Those in favour, **19** Literary agent, **23** Wretchedly, **25** Shoe, **28** Odours, **29** Benefice, **30** Muesli, **31** Statuary.
DOWN: 1 Dapper, **2** Serge, **3** Ride, **4** In store, **6** Nadir, **7** Transport, **8** Pedantry, **11** Span, **14** Dour, **15** Title role, **16** Ivy, **17** Amen, **18** Glow-worm, **20** Rhea, **21** Ailment, **22** Celery, **24** Coral, **26** Haifa, **27** Vent.

30

ACROSS: 1 Bird-fancier, **9** Execute, **10** Windsor, **11** Ass, **12** Seamark, **13** Periwig, **14** Nod, **15** Bambi, **17** Doted, **18** Cakes, **20** Utter, **22** Tip, **24** Outline, **25** Unguent, **26** Tan, **27** Collier, **28** Cottage, **29** Steeplejack.
DOWN: 1 Beer and skittles, **2** Rhubarb, **3** Freak, **4** Newsprint, **5** Ignored, **6** Rise with the lark, **7** Person, **8** Frigid, **16** Mousetrap, **18** Crouch, **19** Suicide, **21** Regatta, **23** Potter, **25** Uncle.

31

ACROSS: 1 Popcorn, **5** Virtue, **9** Smarten, **10** Cracker, **11** Bee, **12** Misanthrope, **13** Gross, **14** Grievance, **16** Defenders, **17** Equal, **19** Correctness, **22** Nut, **23** Denture, **24** Raffish, **26** Levers, **27** Strayed.
DOWN: 1 Postbag, **2** Peace conference, **3** Opt, **4** Nines, **5** Vacancies, **6** Reach, **7** Unknown quantity, **8** Breeze, **12** Mason, **14** Greatness, **15** Views, **16** Decode, **18** Latched, **20** Elude, **21** Earns, **25** Fur.

32

ACROSS: 1 Spanking pace, **8** Trieste, **9** Marbles, **11** Tantamount, **12** Deal, **14** Syringes, **16** Bottle, **17** Raj, **19** Yearns, **21** Taffrail, **24** Buck, **25** Andalusian, **27** Leaflet, **28** Concern, **29** Imprisonment.
DOWN: 1 Spinner, **2** Abstaining, **3** Keel over, **4** Naming, **5** Port, **6** Collect, **7** Status symbol, **10** Silver lining, **13** Confluence, **15** Sat, **18** Jamaican, **20** Acclaim, **22** Aliment, **23** Unites, **26** Blur.

33

ACROSS: 6 Upwardly mobile, **9** States, **10** Proteins, **11** Charcoal, **13** Amazed, **15** Spouse, **17** Gemini, **19** Tissue, **20** Envisage, **22** Apparent, **24** Listen, **26** Crumb of comfort.
DOWN: 1 Hunt the slipper, **2** Swot, **3** Presto, **4** Immolate, **5** Able, **7** Lapels, **8** Lingering death, **12** Roots, **14** Alias, **16** Skeleton, **18** Septic, **21** Volume, **23** Army, **25** Show.

34

ACROSS: 1 Majestic, **5** Dances, **9** Contract, **10** Planet, **12** Else, **13** Underwater, **15** Current events, **19** Permanent wave, **23** Thoroughly, **25** Warp, **28** Arabic, **29** Disabled, **30** Hatter, **31** Agitator.
DOWN: 1 Mocker, **2** Jones, **3** Surf, **4** Incense, **6** Allow, **7** Constance, **8** Satirist, **11** Feat, **14** Area, **15** Cormorant, **16** Nun, **17** Veal, **18** Spot cash, **20** Ergo, **21** Telling, **22** Spider, **24** Opine, **26** Allot, **27** Cast.

35

ACROSS: 1 Body and soul, **9** Tobacco, **10** Sultana, **11** Rot, **12** Milkman, **13** Riggers, **14** Spa, **15** Lucky, **17** Diary, **18** Padre, **20** Tired, **22** Dew, **24** Request, **25** Dislike, **26** Oar, **27** Sweeten, **28** Another, **29** King Charles.
DOWN: 1 Bubble-and-squeak, **2** Decimal, **3** Adorn, **4** Destroyer, **5** Obliged, **6** Loaves and fishes, **7** Stamps, **8** Marshy, **16** Catatonic, **18** Parish, **19** Everton, **21** Despoil, **23** Wherry, **25** Drama.

36

ACROSS: 1 Backers, 5 Decent, 9 Amusing, 10 Stature, 11 Tot, 12 Established, 13 Beret, 14 Sharp-eyed, 16 Strangled, 17 Point, 19 Priestcraft, 22 Elf, 23 Realist, 24 Outside, 26 Stupor, 27 Amnesia.
DOWN: 1 Bran-tub, 2 Counter-irritant, 3 Eli, 4 Sight, 5 Dashboard, 6 Coati, 7 Naughty nineties, 8 Tended, 12 Eaten, 14 Solicitor, 15 Pipit, 16 Superb, 18 Taffeta, 20 Skimp, 21 Aroma, 25 Tin.

37

ACROSS: 1 Sleeping pill, 8 Idiotic, 9 Torment, 11 Ghibelline, 12 Kiwi, 14 Nightcap, 16 Tingle, 17 Rap, 19 Ankles, 21 Lavender, 24 Eden, 25 Joss-sticks, 27 Lucerne, 28 Fragile, 29 Up one's sleeve.
DOWN: 1 Sailing, 2 Entreaties, 3 Peculiar, 4 Noting, 5 Port, 6 Leering, 7 Virginia reel, 10 Tripe-dresser, 13 Licentiate, 15 Pal, 18 Parsifal, 20 Kneecap, 22 Decline, 23 Boreas, 26 Grin.

38

ACROSS: 6 Usual signature, 9 Shaken, 10 Vicarage, 11 Shoppers, 13 Infamy, 15 Boodle, 17 Detain, 19 Talent, 20 Arcadian, 22 Converse, 24 Trilby, 26 Street musician.
DOWN: 1 Push the boat out, 2 Junk, 3 Glance, 4 Inactive, 5 Stir, 7 Invest, 8 Regimental band, 12 Probe, 14 Fraud, 16 Literate, 18 Gateau, 21 Catkin, 23 View, 25 Iris.

39

ACROSS: 1 Hosepipe, 5 Barber, 9 Audition, 10 Panama, 12 Tank, 13 Machinates, 15 French mustard, 19 Traffic warden, 23 Preference, 25 Alto, 28 Afloat, 29 Receiver, 30 Entity, 31 Startled.
DOWN: 1 Hearty, 2 Sudan, 3 Pity, 4 Prosaic, 6 Again, 7 Boat-train, 8 Roadside, 11 Chum, 14 Beef, 15 Flageolet, 16 How, 17 Soda, 18 Stoppage, 20 Chew, 21 Ancient, 22 Torrid, 24 Exact, 26 Level, 27 Dear.

40

ACROSS: 1 Shortcoming, 9 Pivotal, 10 Treadle, 11 Low, 12 Cannery, 13 Iterate, 14 See, 15 Limit, 17 Great, 18 Codes, 20 Laden, 22 Hog, 24 Payment, 25 Antique, 26 Asp, 27 Edition, 28 Pilfers, 29 Silly season.
DOWN: 1 Seven deadly sins, 2 Oatmeal, 3 Tally, 4 Outwitted, 5 Iceberg, 6 God Save The Queen, 7 Spaces, 8 Deceit, 16 Militancy, 18 Copper, 19 Special, 21 Nettles, 23 Greasy, 25 Apple.

41

ACROSS: 1 Pointed, **5** Appeal, **9** Remorse, **10** Thinker, **11** Mad, **12** Remonstrate, **13** Drawl, **14** Learnedly, **16** Trenchant, **17** Round, **19** Packing-case, **22** Set, **23** Episode, **24** Pontiff, **26** Unison, **27** Colonel.
DOWN: 1 Pyramid, **2** Immediate action, **3** Tor, **4** Dream, **5** Attendant, **6** Paint, **7** Awkward question, **8** Freely, **12** Relic, **14** Leaf-green, **15** Nurse, **16** Tippet, **18** Dutiful, **20** Irons, **21** Aspic, **25** Nil.

42

ACROSS: 1 Cut and thrust, **8** October, **9** Arising, **11** Abhorrence, **12** Wise, **14** Diseased, **16** Weighs, **17** Nip, **19** Tipple, **21** Pakistan, **24** Oboe, **25** First thing, **27** Gaining, **28** Blossom, **29** Below the belt.
DOWN: 1 Catches, **2** Tabernacle, **3** Norsemen, **4** Trance, **5** Rain, **6** Shining, **7** Hot and strong, **10** Guessing game, **13** Heliotrope, **15** Dip, **18** Passable, **20** Profile, **22** Twin-set, **23** Fidget, **26** Lino.

43

ACROSS: 6 Unpleasantness, **9** Stores, **10** Excision, **11** Idolised, **13** Bricks, **15** Finish, **17** Prefer, **19** Veneer, **20** Informal, **22** Denounce, **24** Assume, **26** Stage direction.
DOWN: 1 Quite different, **2** Spur, **3** Senses, **4** Snack-bar, **5** Ants, **7** Steady, **8** Shock treatment, **12** Lance, **14** Infer, **16** Serenade, **18** Linear, **21** France, **23** Orgy, **25** Suit.

44

ACROSS: 1 Conifer, **5** Rustle, **9** Anagram, **10** Farrago, **11** Sea, **12** Contraption, **13** Canoe, **14** Hindsight, **16** Penitence, **17** Erupt, **19** Appropriate, **22** See, **23** Candied, **24** Applied, **26** Wealth, **27** Expense.
DOWN: 1 Classic, **2** Neat as ninepence, **3** Far, **4** Roman, **5** Reference, **6** Scrap, **7** Leading question, **8** Bonnet, **12** Chest, **14** Hundredth, **15** Scene, **16** Prance, **18** Treadle, **20** Oriel, **21** Awake, **25** Pip.

45

ACROSS: 1 Rabbit-warren, **8** Offhand, **9** Lambent, **11** Insulation, **12** Lift, **14** Sergeant, **16** Frugal, **17** God, **19** Cogent, **21** Night out, **24** Idea, **25** Compatriot, **27** Nothing, **28** Top-soil, **29** Trade surplus.
DOWN: 1 Refuser, **2** By all means, **3** Inditing, **4** Willow, **5** Ramp, **6** Evening, **7** Conic section, **10** Tittle-tattle, **13** Archetypal, **15** Ton, **18** Disputer, **20** Greater, **22** Ominous, **23** Dodges, **26** Wind.

46

ACROSS: 6 Ill-gotten gains, 9 Whinge, 10 Emissary, 11 Affected, 13 Author, 15 Ragged, 17 Geneva, 19 Stance, 20 Property, 22 Diameter, 24 Temper, 26 Nervous tension.
DOWN: 1 Right first time, 2 Flan, 3 Molest, 4 Intimate, 5 Dais, 7 Tweeds, 8 No room at the inn, 12 Elgin, 14 There, 16 Eventful, 18 Spirit, 21 Outing, 23 Move, 25 Main.

47

ACROSS: 1 Colorado, 5 Status, 9 Ordnance, 10 Museum, 12 Crew, 13 Unpoetical, 15 Crazy pavement, 19 Wild and woolly, 23 Freeholder, 25 Camp, 28 Cattle, 29 Dialogue, 30 Darken, 31 Skinhead.
DOWN: 1 Crouch, 2 Ladle, 3 Reap, 4 Decency, 6 Trust, 7 Treachery, 8 Simulate, 11 Coda, 14 Gaza, 15 Collector, 16 Pew, 17 Eels, 18 Two-faced, 20 Dole, 21 Obelisk, 22 Append, 24 Halve, 26 Argue, 27 Elan.

48

ACROSS: 1 Theatre-goer, 9 Hacksaw, 10 Epergne, 11 Sin, 12 Relieve, 13 Trailer, 14 Bus, 15 Nesta, 17 Tarry, 18 Tapes, 20 Bream, 22 Err, 24 Promise, 25 Denotes, 26 Rio, 27 Solvent, 28 Starred, 29 Modern dress.
DOWN: 1 Ticklish problem, 2 Eastern, 3 Tawse, 4 Eventuate, 5 Overact, 6 Regular features, 7 Cherub, 8 Nearly, 16 Subverter, 18 Typist, 19 Stipend, 21 Mandate, 23 Reside, 25 Dosed.

49

ACROSS: 1 Durable, 5 Pastor, 9 Big-head, 10 Arbiter, 11 Set, 12 Meritorious, 13 Stain, 14 Fireworks, 16 Underhand, 17 Toxic, 19 Cartography, 22 Rue, 23 Inn sign, 24 Pannier, 26 Essene, 27 Lottery.
DOWN: 1 Debases, 2 Rights and wrongs, 3 Bee, 4 Elder, 5 Plastered, 6 Sober, 7 Outdoor exercise, 8 Crisis, 12 Minor, 14 Fragrance, 15 Witty, 16 Urchin, 18 Clearly, 20 Oxide, 21 Pupil, 25 Net.

50

ACROSS: 1 Shopping list, 8 Rosette, 9 Cadmium, 11 Viewfinder, 12 Amps, 14 Discount, 16 Torrid, 17 Gem, 19 Glance, 21 Earpiece, 24 Eats, 25 Categorist, 27 Succour, 28 Aviator, 29 Here and there.
DOWN: 1 Sisters, 2 Out of touch, 3 Preening, 4 Nickel, 5 Lode, 6 Swimmer, 7 Gravediggers, 10 Misadventure, 13 Compromise, 15 Tee, 18 Make fast, 20 Article, 22 Epistle, 23 Barren, 26 Pole.

51

ACROSS: 6 Affairs of state, **9** Adored, **10** Allegory, **11** Anchored, **13** Tiptoe, **15** Double, **17** Assent, **19** Bidden, **20** Answered, **22** Intaglio, **24** Entice, **26** Cross-reference.
DOWN: 1 Hardened sinner, **2** Afar, **3** Hinder, **4** Afflatus, **5** Stag, **7** Shandy, **8** Turn of the Screw, **12** Hound, **14** Piece, **16** Landlord, **18** Pay-off, **21** Steers, **23** Also, **25** Tone.

52

ACROSS: 1 Colossal, **5** Propel, **9** Mystique, **10** Effect, **12** Oars, **13** Intolerant, **15** Across the road, **19** Rogues' gallery, **23** Balustrade, **25** Span, **28** Beaker, **29** Ligament, **30** Eleven, **31** Agonised.
DOWN: 1 Common, **2** Laser, **3** Skin, **4** Alumnus, **6** Rifle, **7** Predatory, **8** Latitude, **11** Hoot, **14** True, **15** Angel-cake, **16** Spa, **17** Eden, **18** Probable, **20** Garb, **21** Lodging, **22** United, **24** Siege, **26** Press, **27** Barn.

53

ACROSS: 1 Full of beans, **9** Miracle, **10** Skipper, **11** Ash, **12** Rewound, **13** Overrun, **14** Ell, **15** Enter, **17** Those, **18** Pears, **20** Oscar, **22** Nap, **24** Endless, **25** Shimmer, **26** Sot, **27** Theatre, **28** Rompers, **29** Sprout wings.
DOWN: 1 Farewell address, **2** Lecture, **3** Oread, **4** Bishopric, **5** Aliment, **6** Superior numbers, **7** Emerge, **8** Prince, **16** Trousseau, **18** Pretty, **19** Sweater, **21** Railman, **23** Perish, **25** Straw.

54

ACROSS: 1 Cambric, **5** Thrush, **9** Monitor, **10** Gumdrop, **11** Elm, **12** Countenance, **13** Tense, **14** Provision, **16** Tractable, **17** Ingle, **19** Unmentioned, **22** Ice, **23** Hashish, **24** Mud-flat, **26** Endear, **27** Hipster.
DOWN: 1 Comment, **2** Monumental mason, **3** Rut, **4** Corfu, **5** Tight-rope, **6** Roman, **7** Shrinking violet, **8** Spleen, **12** Cleft, **14** Publisher, **15** Iliad, **16** Touchy, **18** Elector, **20** Noise, **21** Nymph, **25** Dip.

55

ACROSS: 1 Rocking-horse, **8** Andante, **9** Origins, **11** Speciality, **12** Alec, **14** Masseuse, **16** Person, **17** Elm, **19** Nipper, **21** Faceless, **24** Oust, **25** Troubadour, **27** Student, **28** Edition, **29** Metric system.
DOWN: 1 Redress, **2** Cantilever, **3** Idealise, **4** Grotto, **5** Omit, **6** Stifles, **7** Parsimonious, **10** Second string, **13** Federalist, **15** Elf, **18** Maturely, **20** Posture, **22** Egotism, **23** Critic, **26** Wear.

56

ACROSS: 6 On one's hind legs, 9 Inform, 10 Lonesome, 11 Response, 13 Amazon, 15 On time, 17 Second, 19 Byword, 20 Telegram, 22 Vaulting, 24 Sewage, 26 Merry and bright.

DOWN: 1 Down memory lane, 2 Polo, 3 Vermin, 4 Inundate, 5 Alas, 7 Halter, 8 Game of draughts, 12 Patio, 14 Along, 16 Madrigal, 18 Staged, 21 Lustre, 23 Lyre, 25 Wage.

57

ACROSS: 1 Half-moon, 5 Probes, 9 Penknife, 10 Cupola, 12 Ewes, 13 Refinement, 15 Blankety blank, 19 Figure-skating, 23 Songstress, 25 Slap, 28 One-way, 29 Departed, 30 Tester, 31 Needless.

DOWN: 1 Hyphen, 2 Lunge, 3 Mint, 4 Off-peak, 6 Route, 7 Boomerang, 8 Swastika, 11 Mist, 14 Lair, 15 Beginners, 16 Elk, 17 Brim, 18 Offshoot, 20 Spry, 21 Austere, 22 Spades, 24 Shake, 26 Litre, 27 Wand.

58

ACROSS: 1 Miss nothing, 9 Radiate, 10 All over, 11 Can, 12 Collide, 13 Shifted, 14 Rio, 15 Motto, 17 Liege, 18 Rates, 20 Meets, 22 Age, 24 Dress up, 25 Shavers, 26 Ice, 27 Chorale, 28 Railway, 29 Danger money.

DOWN: 1 Middle of the road, 2 Stadium, 3 Niece, 4 Transpose, 5 Ill-will, 6 Give the game away, 7 Grocer, 8 Cradle, 16 Timepiece, 18 Reduce, 19 Sustain, 21 Station, 23 Essays, 25 Serum.

59

ACROSS: 1 Comical, 5 Decide, 9 Ammonia, 10 Surface, 11 Sun, 12 Detrimental, 13 Sport, 14 Apartment, 16 Composure, 17 Pound, 19 Indulgently, 22 Tap, 23 Cleanse, 24 Survive, 26 Aspect, 27 Artiste.

DOWN: 1 Chassis, 2 Moment of madness, 3 Con, 4 Least, 5 Dissipate, 6 Curse, 7 Draw the curtains, 8 Pellet, 12 Ditto, 14 Amusement, 15 Topsy, 16 Clinch, 18 Deplete, 20 Lance, 21 Tosca, 25 Rat.

60

ACROSS: 1 Monkey-puzzle, 8 Manx cat, 9 Slavish, 11 Rhinoceros, 12 Purr, 14 Lunatics, 16 Frieze, 17 Ham, 19 Gloomy, 21 Testator, 24 Eggs, 25 Solidified, 27 Non-stop, 28 Thicken, 29 School-friend.

DOWN: 1 Mansion, 2 Nick of time, 3 Entrench, 4 Piston, 5 Zeal, 6 Leisure, 7 Emerald green, 10 Horse-trading, 13 Fratricide, 15 Sat, 18 Mediator, 20 Organic, 22 Tricked, 23 Gospel, 26 Otto.

61

ACROSS: 6 Open University, **9** Agreed, **10** Gendarme, **11** Portrait, **13** Simple, **15** Nation, **17** Onager, **19** Finery, **20** Bird-lime, **22** Overdose, **24** Curing, **26** Crest of the wave.
DOWN: 1 Long John Silver, **2** Bede, **3** Tundra, **4** Tennyson, **5** Asia, **7** Ingots, **8** Timely reminder, **12** Tithe, **14** Mogul, **16** Oxymoron, **18** Object, **21** Racket, **23** Rasp, **25** Roam.

62

ACROSS: 1 Margrave, **5** Emoted, **9** Seminary, **10** Across, **12** Lath, **13** Four-poster, **15** Crossed in love, **19** Excuse-me dance, **23** Articulate, **25** Amen, **28** Trivet, **29** Kangaroo, **30** Dreamy, **31** Stagnate.
DOWN: 1 Muscle, **2** Remit, **3** Rung, **4** Various, **6** Macao, **7** Two-stroke, **8** Deserter, **11** Bred, **14** Toes, **15** Cicatrice, **16** Eye, **17** None, **18** Departed, **20** Mile, **21** Detract, **22** Invoke, **24** Cream, **26** Maria, **27** Agog.

63

ACROSS: 1 Playing-card, **9** Precede, **10** Biretta, **11** Pie, **12** Insight, **13** Traders, **14** Tar, **15** Rogue, **17** Twine, **18** Argon, **20** Owned, **22** Hat, **24** Furtive, **25** Risotto, **26** Sue, **27** Cheroot, **28** Inuring, **29** Sleeping-bag.
DOWN: 1 Pleasure gardens, **2** Avenger, **3** Inept, **4** Go-between, **5** Abreast, **6** Do the right thing, **7** Sprint, **8** Hassle, **16** Goose-step, **18** Affect, **19** Noisome, **21** Disturb, **23** Trough, **25** Reign.

64

ACROSS: 1 Post-bag, **5** Select, **9** Rooster, **10** Rapport, **11** Bit, **12** Absenteeism, **13** Ennui, **14** Hamburger, **16** Algonquin, **17** Gross, **19** Disaffected, **22** Nag, **23** Crusado, **24** Release, **26** Behead, **27** Entreat.
DOWN: 1 Parable, **2** Sporting gesture, **3** Bat, **4** Gores, **5** Strongman, **6** Lapse, **7** Closing-down sale, **8** Stumer, **12** Align, **14** Household, **15** Urged, **16** Addict, **18** Suggest, **20** Frame, **21** Three, **25** Lot.

65

ACROSS: 1 Rough justice, **8** Imputes, **9** Resound, **11** Tarantella, **12** Dame, **14** Resigned, **16** Wheeze, **17** Dig, **19** Poison, **21** Portable, **24** Role, **25** Possessing, **27** Seminal, **28** Moisten, **29** Screen-writer.
DOWN: 1 Reports, **2** Up to no good, **3** Hastened, **4** Unruly, **5** Task, **6** Courage, **7** Winter sports, **10** Diesel engine, **13** White skirt, **15** Dip, **18** Gossamer, **20** Islamic, **22** Blister, **23** Poplin, **26** Knee.

66

ACROSS: 6 Throw overboard, **9** Pastel, **10** Sting-ray, **11** Stampede, **13** Astute, **15** Outcry, **17** Bygone, **19** Advent, **20** Overhead, **22** Overdone, **24** Derive, **26** Brothers in arms.

DOWN: 1 Straits of Dover, **2** Brat, **3** Twelve, **4** Ordinary, **5** Song, **7** Vessel, **8** Reap the harvest, **12** Mitre, **14** Tooth, **16** Rationed, **18** Cowers, **21** Ending, **23** Ruth, **25** Rare.

67

ACROSS: 1 Seascape, **5** Stupid, **9** Revision, **10** Morass, **12** Kiln, **13** Legislator, **15** Clear the decks, **19** Advanced level, **23** Permission, **25** Data, **28** Whoops, **29** Dominant, **30** Result, **31** Stippled.

DOWN: 1 Shrike, **2** Anvil, **3** Cost, **4** Pioneer, **6** Troll, **7** Practical, **8** Distrust, **11** Dish, **14** Keen, **15** Cavernous, **16** Ted, **17** Dove, **18** Manpower, **20** Ease, **21** Lookout, **22** Parted, **24** Impel, **26** Avail, **27** Limp.

68

ACROSS: 1 All-star cast, **9** Trained, **10** Absolve, **11** Aid, **12** Conical, **13** Snippet, **14** Opt, **15** Table, **17** Scour, **18** Other, **20** Midas, **22** Ebb, **24** Forages, **25** Marquis, **26** Hoe, **27** Collide, **28** Dribble, **29** Smell danger.

DOWN: 1 Against the rules, **2** Linocut, **3** Tidal, **4** Roadstead, **5** Assails, **6** Telephone number, **7** Stucco, **8** Sector, **16** Bombshell, **18** Office, **19** Ragtime, **21** Surfing, **23** Bushel, **25** Media.

69

ACROSS: 1 Primula, **5** Strike, **9** Deviant, **10** Taffeta, **11** Owl, **12** Accelerator, **13** Kedge, **14** Imitation, **16** Grandsire, **17** Pagan, **19** Participate, **22** Get, **23** Evangel, **24** Stamina, **26** Sentry, **27** Eclogue.

DOWN: 1 Padlock, **2** Invalid carriage, **3** Una, **4** Attic, **5** Satellite, **6** Refer, **7** Keep things going, **8** Patron, **12** Ahead, **14** Initially, **15** Apple, **16** Gopher, **18** Nut-case, **20** Ingot, **21** Aisle, **25** All.

70

ACROSS: 1 Spinal column, **8** Ammeter, **9** Sparrow, **11** Salamander, **12** Marc, **14** Parodies, **16** Little, **17** Ran, **19** Remote, **21** Gimcrack, **24** Link, **25** Malignance, **27** Another, **28** Iterate, **29** United States.

DOWN: 1 Similar, **2** Intimidate, **3** Arranger, **4** Cashew, **5** Lead, **6** Mordant, **7** Sarsaparilla, **10** Wicket-keeper, **13** Disconcert, **15** Sag, **18** Nihilist, **20** Monsoon, **22** Anneals, **23** Barred, **26** Shot.

71
ACROSS: 6 Identical twins, 9 Shrink, 10 Priority, 11 Perforce, 13 Uncoil, 15 France, 17 Belong, 19 Broken, 20 Traction, 22 Adherent, 24 Scruff, 26 Hypnotic trance.
DOWN: 1 Michael Faraday, 2 Peri, 3 Stoker, 4 Altitude, 5 Ewer, 7 Capped, 8 Nothing to offer, 12 Frank, 14 Clout, 16 Confetti, 18 Static, 21 Absurd, 23 Erne, 25 Ring.

72
ACROSS: 1 Trollope, 5 Cajole, 9 Chandler, 10 Street, 12 Leek, 13 Nasturtium, 15 Horse chestnut, 19 Courtesy title, 23 Right angle, 25 Seam, 28 Italic, 29 Obdurate, 30 Nestle, 31 Eyebrows.
DOWN: 1 Tackle, 2 Orate, 3 Lady, 4 Prelate, 6 Altar, 7 Obedience, 8 Estimate, 11 Itch, 14 Fret, 15 Hour-glass, 16 Coy, 17 Site, 18 Scorpion, 20 Sink, 21 Tallboy, 22 Embers, 24 Trial, 26 Erato, 27 Dumb.

73
ACROSS: 1 Firm friends, 9 Rousing, 10 Temping, 11 Hue, 12 Oddment, 13 Redskin, 14 Hot, 15 Tepee, 17 Cross, 18 Brood, 20 Opted, 22 Nod, 24 Licence, 25 Accuser, 26 Nap, 27 Averted, 28 Aground, 29 Modern times.
DOWN: 1 Foundation cream, 2 Raiment, 3 Fight, 4 Interject, 5 Nomadic, 6 Stick to one's guns, 7 Brooch, 8 Agents, 16 Provender, 18 Ballad, 19 Denoted, 21 Decorum, 23 Deride, 25 Apart.

74
ACROSS: 1 Proctor, 5 Combat, 9 Endmost, 10 Outdoor, 11 Zoo, 12 Cold-blooded, 13 Lifer, 14 Paralysis, 16 Revisited, 17 Sahib, 19 Mountaineer, 22 Her, 23 Eminent, 24 Vanilla, 26 Hectic, 27 Imposed.
DOWN: 1 Pretzel, 2 Odds-on favourite, 3 Too, 4 Ratel, 5 Clobbered, 6 Motto, 7 As old as the hills, 8 Grades, 12 Cares, 14 Patriotic, 15 Loser, 16 Rammed, 18 Barmaid, 20 Trent, 21 Envoi, 25 Nip.

75
ACROSS: 1 Jack-in-office, 8 Pageant, 9 Algebra, 11 Chatterbox, 12 Scot, 14 Suspense, 16 Repeal, 17 Try, 19 Unmask, 21 Aesthete, 24 Toga, 25 Effrontery, 27 Enclose, 28 Isolate, 29 Clear-sighted.
DOWN: 1 Jigsaws, 2 Chartreuse, 3 Interest, 4 Orator, 5 Figs, 6 Cubicle, 7 Space shuttle, 10 Artillerymen, 13 Setting out, 15 Era, 18 Yearling, 20 Magical, 22 Emerald, 23 Offers, 26 Soda.

76

ACROSS: 6 Undergo repairs, **9** Sketch, **10** Ensemble, **11** Stranded, **13** Narrow, **15** Native, **17** Closet, **19** Astral, **20** Aircraft, **22** Daughter, **24** Theory, **26** Mental exercise.
DOWN: 1 Bucket and spade, **2** Adit, **3** Orchid, **4** Personal, **5** Warm, **7** Overdo, **8** Rule out of order, **12** Actor, **14** Riser, **16** Volatile, **18** Matrix, **21** Retire, **23** Gate, **25** Evil.

77

ACROSS: 1 Gruesome, **5** Nimbus, **9** Mobilise, **10** Rennet, **12** Lone, **13** Safe-blower, **15** Going straight, **19** After a fashion, **23** Overburden, **25** Peer, **28** Tribal, **29** Struggle, **30** Digest, **31** Crescent.
DOWN: 1 Gamble, **2** Urban, **3** Silk, **4** Mustang, **6** Ideal, **7** Bandwagon, **8** Saturate, **11** Left, **14** Liar, **15** Gathering, **16** Spa, **17** Acid, **18** Cavorted, **20** Fort, **21** Sweeter, **22** Urgent, **24** Brass, **26** Eagle, **27** Fuss.

78

ACROSS: 1 Over and over, **9** Eyelets, **10** Clogged, **11** Eva, **12** Fairest, **13** Leaflet, **14** Run, **15** Thing, **17** Error, **18** Basis, **20** Treat, **22** Rot, **24** Harrier, **25** Morocco, **26** Moo, **27** Shackle, **28** Raining, **29** Turn the tide.
DOWN: 1 Obedient servant, **2** Element, **3** Asset, **4** Decalogue, **5** Violate, **6** Regular practice, **7** Heifer, **8** Editor, **16** Interment, **18** Behest, **19** Sticker, **21** Termini, **23** Though, **25** Morse.

79

ACROSS: 1 Rescued, **5** Arcade, **9** Memento, **10** Prosper, **11** Art, **12** Pondicherry, **13** Twill, **14** Mannequin, **16** Aggregate, **17** Views, **19** Proceedings, **22** Ode, **23** Another, **24** Valance, **26** Unclad, **27** Loosely.
DOWN: 1 Rampant, **2** Something to go on, **3** Urn, **4** Drown, **5** Appliance, **6** Cloth, **7** Departure lounge, **8** Crayon, **12** Pulse, **14** Meandered, **15** Eaves, **16** Appeal, **18** Scenery, **20** Ethel, **21** Novel, **25** Leo.

80

ACROSS: 1 Back and forth, **8** Retract, **9** Burnish, **11** Trendiness, **12** Sign, **14** Canalise, **16** Bonnet, **17** Ham, **19** Images, **21** Tangling, **24** Chap, **25** Chucker-out, **27** Eleanor, **28** Evasive, **29** Drag one's feet.
DOWN: 1 Between, **2** Chandelier, **3** Astonish, **4** Debase, **5** Ogre, **6** Tuition, **7** Arctic Circle, **10** Hang together, **13** Congregate, **15** Eat, **18** Marchers, **20** Amateur, **22** Ironist, **23** Charon, **26** Snug.

81

ACROSS: 6 Ring in one's ears, 9 Impede, 10 Whodunit, 11 Pilaster, 13 Repine, 15 Effect, 17 Person, 19 Collie, 20 Passer-by, 22 Disburse, 24 Catnap, 26 Wedding present.

DOWN: 1 From side to side, 2 Anne, 3 Silent, 4 Recourse, 5 Menu, 7 Onward, 8 Reigning beauty, 12 Awful, 14 Paste, 16 Cheering, 18 Upkeep, 21 Socket, 23 Body, 25 Then.

82

ACROSS: 1 Escalope, 5 Drowse, 9 Bathrobe, 10 Sleeve, 12 Ride, 13 Convergent, 15 Flesh and blood, 19 Period costume, 23 Roundabout, 25 Park, 28 Oracle, 29 Algerian, 30 Seeker, 31 Trumpery.

DOWN: 1 Embark, 2 Cited, 3 Lord, 4 Pibroch, 6 Ruler, 7 Woebegone, 8 Eventide, 11 Oven, 14 Hero, 15 Fortunate, 16 Ado, 17 Blue, 18 Spurious, 20 Cube, 21 Squalor, 22 Skinny, 24 Delve, 26 Alive, 27 Beam.

83

ACROSS: 1 Grease paint, 9 Ontario, 10 Resolve, 11 Oaf, 12 Menaced, 13 Enliven, 14 Two, 15 Egret, 17 Risen, 18 Wrong, 20 Under, 22 Orb, 24 Lowland, 25 Roasted, 26 Eva, 27 Outfall, 28 Thimble, 29 Ready tongue.

DOWN: 1 Get into hot water, 2 Earache, 3 Snood, 4 Perfected, 5 Insular, 6 Television table, 7 Commit, 8 Pennon, 16 Roundelay, 18 Wallop, 19 Granada, 21 Reading, 23 Budget, 25 Ratio.

84

ACROSS: 1 Deposit, 5 Stalls, 9 Syringa, 10 Angular, 11 Air, 12 Contentious, 13 Tribe, 14 Presently, 16 Important, 17 Dress, 19 Seismometer, 22 Ale, 23 Cutting, 24 Stealth, 26 Briton, 27 Essayed.

DOWN: 1 Distant, 2 Portrait painter, 3 Sun, 4 Twain, 5 Statement, 6 Argot, 7 Lily of the valley, 8 Crusty, 12 Clear, 14 Ptarmigan, 15 Elder, 16 Insect, 18 Seethed, 20 Moist, 21 Taste, 25 Ems.